How To Earn Your No-Code Ham License

By

Donald L. Stoner, W6TNS

The National Amateur Radio Association
P.O. Box 598
Redmond, WA 98073-0598

The *Introduction Chapter* is also available in a document called *Amateur Radio-King of Hobbies*. Single reprints are available from The National Amateur Radio Association at no cost. Quantity reprints of this material, for distribution by clubs, manufacturers and Amateur Radio dealers are available at nominal cost. Contact the publisher for more information.

First Printing 1993
Cover—Photos by Gary Kaplan, equipment courtesy of Kenwood and Alinco
Cover Layout—Debra Bundy
Composition—Proofreading by Sandra Zimmey

9   8   7   6   5   4   3   2   1

Table of Contents

Foreword

I can't believe it is time to replace the question pool for the Novice and Technician Class license. It just proves that time flies when you're having fun.

When I wrote the first version of this book, no one had any idea the Technician class license (the so-called no-code license) would be so well accepted and accomplish so perfectly its purpose. It is one of the greatest success stories in the long, proud history of the Amateur Radio Service.

What was the purpose of revising the rules to drop Morse code as an entry level requirement? The public had come to perceive Morse as a rather unpleasant hazing ritual that must be mastered if one wanted to become a ham. As a result, growth in our fraternity was stagnant, young people were disinterested, and the median age of Amateurs increased with each passing year.

Those of us at the forefront of the "no-code movement" recognized that a code-free license could be used as a *marketing tool* to introduce the public to the wonderful world of Amateur Radio. We looked upon the license as a way to "get the hook in and set," to use a fishing metaphor. And it worked!

The first no-code Technician class licenses were issued in March of 1991. By the end of 1992, almost 50,000 Technician licenses had been granted. As a result, the Amateur population should exceed 600,000 sometime during 1993. Very clearly, the Technician license will be the predominant class in the coming years.

The National Amateur Radio Association (NARA) was formed to represent the interest of these newcomers. It is the only national organization devoted specifically to the interests of Novice and Technician class Amateurs. In the coming years there will be many events and FCC actions that critically affect the status and privileges of the newcomer. I invite you to join this growing organization and receive our member publication, *The Amateur Radio Communicator*. We need your support, and membership is only $10.00 per year—that's a real bargain for a national organization which represents your interests in Washington.

But I digress. Before I started the first version of this book, I spent quite a bit of time loitering in the Seattle radio stores. I eavesdropped on those who browsed the book counter, and noted their comments when they thumbed through testing manuals. The material available to them varied from simple memorization manuals to elaborate works that brought comments like "Wow—do I have to learn all this stuff to be a ham?" Like Goldilocks, I think I've found the right porridge. I explain the theory behind the question in an easy-to-understand matter.

This time around we are calling the book "How To Earn Your No-Code Ham License." It has just the right amount of material—just what you need to know to earn your license, but not so much that you are befuddled by information not required to pass the test.

You will notice the material has been arranged in a unique manner which was developed by NARA for their training manuals. The various question pools are arranged into nine main subjects areas. We've used these subjects as the heading for Chapters One through Nine. Each chapter provides the basic theory behind the questions so that you need not simply memorize the answers. At the end of various paragraphs, you will find the number of a question, or questions, that the preceding paragraph explains. Then, at the end of the chapter, we provide all the questions for that section of the pool, numbered in the same manner. The "N" and "T" indicate questions from the Novice and Technician pools. The number following this alpha character is the subelement and also, not coincidentally, the chapter number for the book. The remaining alphanumeric characters represent the subelement and question numbers.

You should study the book by carefully reading each chapter. When you run across a question number at the end of a paragraph, look up the question. Then see if what you have just read has taught you what you need to know in order to answer the question.

After you have done this a few times, you will want to read the entire chapter, then "take the test" by reviewing the questions at the end of the chapter. By the way, don't write on the book. Rather, use a writing tablet or piece of paper. Other members of your family, friends and acquaintances, may wish to also take the test. Once you have completed reviewing the questions refer to the correct answer key at the end of the book.

If I may be allowed another "plug," The National Amateur Radio Association has excellent computerized training and testing software for use on either MS-DOS machines or Macintosh computers.

One final word before you start down the path to a whole new world. The Federal Communications Commission Rules and Regulations specify that a new pool of test questions be introduced *every four years*, for each class of Amateur license. Things change, particularly in the area of regulations, and replacing the questions allows material to be brought up to date on a reasonably regular basis.

Many people think that since the FCC oversees our Amateur Radio operations, they also create the question pools. But this is *definitely* not the case. Not only has the FCC turned over the testing of potential Amateurs and those wishing to upgrade to a higher class, but Amateurs also create and revise the question pools.

The question pools are created entirely by volunteers from the Amateur Radio community. It starts with a committee of three hams from the National Conference of Volunteer Examiner Coordinators. The current Question Pool Committee consists of Ray Adams, N4BAQ of WCARS, Bart Jahnke, KB9NM, of the American Radio Relay League, and Fred Maia, W5YI of the W5YI Group. They start by soliciting questions from the Amateur Radio fraternity. Then these three people and their helpers select, sort and organize the proposed questions which have been submitted to them. It is a most difficult job for which they receive no compensation. They must make certain that there is no ambiguity, or areas that are open to debate, should someone misunderstand a question and select the wrong answer.

This latest group of questions are the best ever! The Question Pool Committee, and their helpers, have created a valid test that will determine if the applicant is qualified to be an Amateur Radio operator. It is to the Committee, their helpers and those who submitted questions for the pool that this book is dedicated.

The changeover date from the "old questions" to the "new questions" occurs on July 1, 1993. The pool will remain valid until June 30, 1997. If you are planning on studying for the Novice or Technician license, this book contains the pool of questions from which your test questions will be selected during that period.

73, Donald L. Stoner, W6TNS

Introduction

Amateur Radio—The King of Hobbies

To their non-Amateur friends, "hams" are slightly eccentric characters who live in a little world all their own. To their spouse, a ham is the "lunkhead" who gets solder on the carpet and is responsible for enormous electric bills. Neighbors sometimes consider them members of a vast organization dedicated to the violent overthrow of television. All will agree that hams seem to speak in a foreign tongue. But to their fellow hams, an Amateur is simply a person with the most interesting, unusual and rewarding hobby in the world.

Amateurs *are* special and participate in the only hobby, called the Amateur Radio Service, which is regulated by the federal government. Amateurs are given free access to radio frequencies which woud be worth literally billions of dollars to commercial interests.

Indisputably, the world of ham radio provides a thrill and excitement like no other leisure time activity. The only question is, do you have the desire and persistence to earn the right to be called a radio Amateur?

Something For Everyone

Ham radio is actually a large group of sub-hobbies within a single hobby, all tied together by electromagnetic waves. Ham radio can be an escape from the humdrum of everyday life by giving you the means to talk with hams all over the world or do experiments and develop new technologies.

Amateurs have many methods of communication. Most use a microphone since it is the fastest way to convey your thoughts and comments to someone else. Many hams do their "talking" with computers. A few hardy souls even have their own TV stations. Some prefer to use Morse code, claiming it is more relaxing, reliable and the equipment less expensive.

Payload Commander Kathryn D. Sullivan, N5YYZ, is one of several astronauts participating in the Shuttle Amateur Radio Experiment (SAREX).

In all, there are more facets to the hobby than there are on the British Crown jewels! Did you know that Amateurs have their own satellites which support communication all over the world? They can even talk to astronauts (both American and Russian) circling the earth in their space ships. The fastest growing segment of our hobby is the digital group. Through a scheme called packet, you can communicate with tens-of-thousands of other computer buffs.

Who Does It?

Amateurs can be found in all walks of life. Well known political figures, such as Barry Goldwater (K7UGA) and His Majesty King Hussain of Jordan (JY1) are both Amateurs. Dick Rutan (KB7LQS) had an Amateur station aboard "Voyager" when he and Jeanna Yaeger made their famous flight around the world.

Country western fans know the names of picker Chet Atkins, WA4CZD and singer Ronnie Milsap, WB4KCG. Other famous hams include rock guitarist Joe Walsh. Donnie Osmond used to be KA7EVD and Marlon Brando is still FO0GJ (Tahiti). Some of the older readers will remember entertainers Andy Devine and Arthur Godfrey (K4LIB) as well as musicians Pee Wee Hunt and Alvino Rey (W6UK).

What Do Hams Talk About?

Barry Goldwater, KL7UGA, is the elder statesman of Amateur Radio. (CQ Magazine Photo)

Let's look at a few activities that occupy the time of more than 600,000 Americans. Chatting, or "rag-chewing", is the most popular diversion. All hams love to talk! As soon as his feet hit the floor, Sam Ham will flick on his transceiver, even before turning on the coffee pot. Around the nation, other hams are doing the same thing. More often than not, a group of these "early birds" collect in a "round-table". A microphone is passed around via the air waves until it is time for the members to dash off to work. The scene is repeated after supper by some of the more avid members of the clan.

"What do you find to talk about?" hams are often asked. Sex, religion, and politics used to be avoided, but open discussion is quite commonplace these days. Generally, the conversation is less likely to be on technical things than on taking care of the house, car problems and critiquing the latest Steven Spielberg movie.

Hamming On The Highway

Sam Ham might also be interested in another phase of the hobby called *mobile* operation. If so, he probably has a very small compact rig in the family car. As Sam threads his way to the office, he can once again participate in the "round-table" from his rolling radio station. Or, should Sam elect to, he can switch the frequency of his equipment and join in the conversation with a similar group of hams clear across the country.

Public Service

Before you get the idea that Amateurs are just a bunch of chattering magpies, remember that it is called the *Amateur Radio Service*. The original intent was public service and the handling of messages. The majority of Amateurs carry on in the same tradition. Amateurs provide public service without compensation.

Ham radio is also a communication service for self-training and technical experimentation. We are allowed access to priceless radio spectrum on the assumption that Amateurs form a valued pool of skilled communicators that can be tapped during emergencies. It is absolutely essential that we maintain this tradition if we are to retain our frequency allocations throughout the communications spectrum.

The Thrill Of DX'ing

The term *DX* means communicating long distance by radio. The DX-minded ham is an unusual variation of the typical Amateur. Like Sam Ham, our inveterate DX'er rises before dawn. He turns on the station and starts the coffee brewing almost at the same time. However, DX Dan does not jump into a round-table. Instead, he squashes a pair of headphones on his ears and intently tunes the receiver dial to and fro. Several days may come and go without so much as a peep out of DX Dan's powerful transmitter. Then one morning Dan flushes his quarry and a look of grim determination settles across his face. He is listening to the faint rolling dots and dashes of 9N1MM, Father Moran, operating from Katmandu, Nepal! Suddenly, as 9N1MM stands by, Dan's powerful "rig" springs to life and the needles on the transmitter measuring instruments swing into action. Less than one minute later, Dan pushes the telegraph key away and writes down this new contact in his log book.

Most amazing, perhaps, is that DX Dan probably heard many other rare and exotic stations while searching the band for 9N1MM. On a typical morning he may have heard most of the new countries that were formerly districts of the Soviet Union, or Sarawak, Brunei, Mauritius, the Orkney Islands, Qatar, Trucial Oman, and of course the more common countries such as England, Japan, Australia, or New Zealand. But Dan ignored their *CQ* ("I'm looking for a contact") calls in favor of the more elusive Nepal Amateur. He had contacted these other stations long ago. As our inveterate DX'er prepared to dash off to work, he checked off the new conquest. Nepal was number 261 on his list of the more than 300 countries in the world.

To quote Dave Bell, W6AQ (who appeared in the video called *The New World of Amateur Radio*), "When you turn on your radio and get on the air, it's like going fishing. You never know exactly what you are going to catch. That's the thrill of DX."

There's plenty of "wallpaper" in this Amateurs "hamshack."

Ham Radio "Wall Paper"

In addition to the thrill of having "hooked" a new one, Dan will get a material reward also. Hams exchange postcards, called QSL's, which confirm their two-way contacts. Each card carries details such as the date and time of contact, mode of transmission (voice or code), and a signal strength report. Thus, sometime after his contact, Dan will receive a card that he can proudly display on the wall of his ham station.

Ambassadors Of Goodwill

An interesting variation of the DX-minded ham is Ambassador Al. Al "gets his kicks" by conversing with overseas Amateurs, mostly to gain friends and exchange ideas. Although he may never meet one of these hams, he is truly an ambassador of international goodwill. These electronic ambassadors can tell you what the temperature was yesterday in Kuala Lumpur, Malasia, or who is winning the tennis matches in Melbourne, Australia. Al has two or three favorite hams overseas and maintains weekly contact schedules with them. Often they exchange inexpensive gifts, and once in a while they have the opportunity of meeting each other.

Young people make excellent United States "ambassadors of the air waves." By communicating with youth in other countries, they help dispel the myth of the "ugly American", particularly at conventions where DX'ers from around the world congregate.

Radio Repeaters

Have you ever tried to communicate with someone using Citizens Band equipment? Not very effective is it? Ham radio has a couple of features not available to CB'ers. The first is Amateur Radio use of *FM* (frequency modulation) equipment. The reception is crystal clear and you only hear *one station at a time*. Another aspect of FM communications is the use of *repeaters*. These devices consist of a receiver and re-transmitter. Neither FM nor repeaters are allowed on the Citizens Band.

Repeaters are usually installed on mountain tops or on roofs of tall buildings. A repeater picks up signals from hand-helds or mobile two-way radios and resends (or repeats) them on another frequency. The signal range can encompass an area as wide as 100 miles with perfect clarity.

There are more than 12,000 Amateur repeaters on the air in North America. You can drive from coast-to-coast and border-to-border and never be out of range of an Amateur repeater. In an emergency you can always contact someone for help with a two-way radio so small it will fit in your pocket or purse.

Repeaters are great for talking to friends in distant cities. For example, you can be driving around downtown Los Angeles and talk to another station motoring in San Diego. Repeaters also facilitate communication over mountains which would normally shield or block the signals.

Some repeaters even have a telephone access so you can call your spouse and indicate that you will be late for

The Alinco DJ-F1 is a full-feature two-meter transceiver. It has CTCSS, tone squelch and a Touch-Tone™ pad for placing calls through a repeater.

dinner. Many Amateur mobile and hand-held radios have a "Touch Tone" pad just like a regular telephone. This permits you to access the repeater telephone channel and dial a telephone number. Best of all, you don't need to pay money to the local cellular telephone system. A word of caution, however; you can't use the ham bands for business. If you want to call your broker and corner the stock market, you'll need a cellular telephone.

What's An XYL?

For convenience, I have used the male gender in describing the various types of Amateurs. However, men certainly don't have a monopoly on the hobby. Female Amateurs are referred to as YL's or "young ladies". An XYL (not ex-YL) is a married young lady. There is no accurate tabulation, but approximately one out of every thirty hams is female.

Probably the first woman ham was Miss Cecil Powell, secretary to the co-founder of the American Radio Relay League, Hiram Percy Maxim. In 1915, she constructed her own station, learned the code, and became an active Amateur.

Ham Radio In Schools

Amateur Radio is an excellent way to help your students apply the subjects you teach to the "real world." It combines geography, basic science, math, language and communications skills into one hobby. It's one thing to memorize the location of a particular city or country on a map. It's quite another thing to actually talk with someone in that country. An Amateur Radio program in your school can add an exciting dimension to your curriculum. Many schools have already discovered the value of adding ham radio.

Personal Safety

It's an unfortunate fact of life, but personal safety is an important consideration these days. Perhaps you live in the country or you take long trips. Is it necessary for your spouse to be out in the car after dark? Are the children at risk? If so, you might consider Amateur Radio for more than it's hobby or public service aspects.

Many people have purchased cellular telephones to provide a degree of safety in difficult situations. However, if you do not need a cellular telephone for business, then a ham radio will do everything that a phone will do and more. And the cost is right. The air time is free!

In fact, a small two-way, hand-held radio costs about the same as three-months or less of the average cost for operating a cellular phone. As mentioned earlier, there is virtually nowhere in the United States where one cannot contact a radio Amateur, either direct or via a repeater.

Welcome CB'ers!

Since it began, the Amateur Radio Service grew at a steady pace with more newcomers arriving each year. In the early 1970's, the ham population expanded faster than ever before. This was due to interest in the Citizens Band. People were introduced to the wonders of radio communications but wanted something better. Ham radio provided it. Hams talk worldwide, limited only by signal progagation conditions. There are no distance restrictions as in CB. Amateurs use static-free FM radios for local contacts. They can also legally transmit using up to 1500 watts output power in a variety of communication modes rather than being restricted to just a few watts of power on AM or single sideband (SSB).

The shortcomings of CB and the attraction of ham radio has brought many new members into our hobby. Today, probably 20 percent of the existing Amateurs are ex-CB'er's. Amateurs embrace CB "born again" communicators and encourage them to get a ham license.

How About You?

Think you'd like to be a ham? Want to join about three million others worldwide and experience the thrill of communications by ham radio? Anyone can become a licensed Amateur operator. *You don't have to be a United States citizen and there are no age restrictions.* There are six year old Amateurs and senior citizen hams in their nineties.

Many young people are interested in becoming Radio Amateurs. Daniel Savio, AA2GM, of Ridgewood, New Jersey visited NARA at the 1992 Dayton Hamvention.

It's easy, and getting easier every day, to open that first door to the Amateur Service. All you have to do is attend a VE session and pass a simple test.

The Volunteer Examiner Program

Since 1984, Volunteer Examiners have taken over the testing function from the government. All prospective hams are tested by a VE (Volunteer Examiner) team. VECs (Volunteer Examiner Coordinators) have replaced the FCC in the testing function. They develop all examinations and testing guidelines and make them available to the Amateur testing community. Practically every city with a population of 50,000 or more has monthly VEC examinations conducted by volunteers. Under the VEC System, three VEs administer the exams and they must have an Amateur license of a higher class than those being tested.

VEs are systematically accredited and provided Amateur testing information and materials by a VEC. A VEC is an organization established to act as the testing liaison between the VE and the FCC, the agency that issues Amateur licenses. VEs are always happy to have newcomers appear at their testing sessions. The Technician class applicant must be examined under the VEC System and a small testing fee (less than $6.00) is charged to defray the cost of the testing program.

Volunteer Examiner Coordinators have developed a large pool of multiple-choice questions that apply to the things beginning hams should know. All of the questions, even the exact word-for-word multiple-choice answers, are widely published. Copies of these exams, with the correct answers, are available from the National Amateur Radio Association at low cost.

The Technician Class License

Until February 13, 1991, government regulations required that you had to be proficient at copying Morse code to obtain an Amateur license. Actually, communication by Morse is enjoyable and challenging, but it was perceived by the public to be a difficult obstacle.

As a result of this perception, the Federal Communications Commission (FCC) created an entry level of Amateur license. The license is called the *Technician class*, and you *do not* need to learn Morse code to earn this license.

The Technician license is really a "beginner's permit." To earn it, and prove you are qualified to be an Amateur, you still have to pass a written test.

The Technician license gives you full Amateur privileges on the very high frequency (VHF) and ultra-high (UHF) bands including six meters and above. Most satellite and computer communication occur on these bands. With a Technician license you can communicate world-wide using Amateur Radio satellites.

The Technician question pool is a combination of the questions for the Novice class license (called Element 2) and the questions from the previous Technician class license (called Element 3A). The VEs simply administer 55 questions from the two pools according to a selection formula. This formula is stated by the FCC in Part 97 Rules and Regulations for the Amateur Service (available from the National Amateur Radio Association). There are about 700 questions in the Element 2 and 3(A) question pools from which the VE selects for your Technician examination.

Your VE team will select 30 questions from the Element 2 pool and 25 from Element 3(A). Passing Element 2 requires you to answer 22 questions correctly; Element 3(A) requires 19—a total of 41 correct out of 55.

You need not pass both test elements at the same time. You can wait to take the second element. If you fail one element, you still receive credit for the test element passed. The VE team will give you a credit slip, called a *Certificate of Successful Completion of Examination (CSCE)*, good towards the remaining examination element which must be completed within one year. If you don't pass the remaining test element in one year, you lose your credit for the portion passed. The process is very similar to the written test given to obtain a driving license. You study the rules, procedures, and questions and then pass the test.

After you pass the test, your application will be immediately forwarded by the VE team to the VEC who coordinated the testing session. (A copy of your credit certificate must be attached to your application if you claim a previously passed examination element.) The VEC verifies that everything is correct and forwards the material to the FCC. The application is returned to you if you fail the test. It is important to obtain a photocopy of your Certificate of Successful Completion of Examination if you plan to upgrade to a higher class license before your license arrives. The next VE team will require proof you have already passed the examination before testing you further.

You can't go on-the-air until your license arrives. It takes from six to 10 weeks to get your "diploma" from Uncle Sam. The exact time required depends on the work load in Gettysburg, Pennsylvania, where the licenses are processed.

Once you receive your "ticket," the fun begins. The first time you go on the air, your forehead will break out in a cold sweat! You'll forget all the rules of speech and your sentences will be punctuated with "er's" and "uh's." But after a few days of this "affliction" from ham radio "jitters," you'll sound like an ol' timer.

The Technician-Plus License

Once you earn your Technician class license, don't stop there. The next step is the so-called Technician-Plus (for Technician *plus* Morse code). This is not an official term but the jargon seems to have been adopted by hams as well as the term "Tech-Lite," meaning a Technician license without Morse code.

After you have conquered the code, you can advance to the General, Advanced and Extra classes. You no longer have the option of becoming a Novice class operator once you enter via the Technician path. To advance to Tech-Plus you must pass Element 1(A), which is the five words-per-minute telegraphy examination given at a VEC test session. While considered an upgrade, you will not be issued a *different* operator license or call sign by the FCC. Your new privileges will be vested by a *Certificate of Successful Completion of Examination* given to you by the examining team.

Tech-Plus operators additionally obtain operating privileges in segments of the Amateur 80, 40, 15 and 10 meter bands. Most of these bands are for telegraphy, but Tech-Plus operators are permitted voice emission in a portion of the 10-meter band.

Continue to study and improve your knowledge. Remember, a Technician "ticket" is simply a key which opens the first door and allows you to enter a wondrous room with many more doors. There is no "free lunch" in this world. You get what you pay for, whether the currency is sweat or dollars. The Technician license is only the beginning, not the ultimate goal. Plan on learning the Morse code so you can use the other Amateur bands. You'll be glad you did!

The Novice Class

The FCC decided to keep the Novice class operator license in order to provide an alternative entry level license for persons (especially youngsters) who find the telegraphy requirement easier than the more comprehensive written examination for the codeless Technician class operator license.

Novices can operate using Morse code on the 80, 40, 15 and 10-meter bands, voice mode (SSB) on a segment of the 10-meter band and can also use portions of the 222-MHz and 1270-MHz ham bands.

To become a Novice you must pass Element 2 (30 questions) and Element 1(A), the five word-per-minute Morse test. The only difference in taking the Novice rather than the Technician exam is that you will take the five-wpm code test instead of the Technician written theory, Element 3(A).

As a general rule, to engage in worldwide communications, you need at least a Novice or Tech Plus license. "Tech-Lites" can work DX occasionally on six meters. Sometimes transmissions on the six-meter VHF band transmissions travel great distances. With either the Novice or Tech-Plus license you can communicate by voice on the 10-meter Amateur band and by Morse code on other bands. The 10-meter band can carry signals around the world at various times of the year. The 80, 40, and 15-meter bands, where you will use code, have long distance capabilities nearly any hour of the day and night.

Brian C. Sunderman, KB8LCO, of Cincinnati, Ohio, comes from a ham family. His dad, Clem, is KA8QFK and brother Tim is KB8ENN.

Dah-Dit, Dah-Dit

It's easy to learn Morse code. You can use a personal computer (with NARA programs like HamWare and Morse Academy for the PC), listen to on-the-air code practice or use audio cassette code training tapes. Morse code seems difficult at first, but is actually quite easy to learn. All it takes is a bit of practice.

Your Examiners are allowed considerable freedom to determine if you have passed the Morse code test. At examination time you will be sent at least five minutes of Morse code at five words-per-minute. The only guidelines for examiners are: (1) they must be convinced and certify that you can receive the International Morse code at five words-per-minute during a transmission of at least five minutes; and (2) the text transmitted must contain forty-three different characters. These are all the letters of the alphabet, all numerals 0-9, four punctuation marks (period, comma, question mark and slant bar) and three operating procedure signs (AR, BT and SK). While not required, most code examinations take the form of a typical Morse code exchange between two on-the-air Amateurs. It's unlikely you will be asked to send Morse code, since the FCC has taken the position that operators who can receive Morse code can also send it.

Some Examiners will ask you to correctly copy 25 characters in a row (punctuation, numerals and prosigns count as two characters) to determine if you can copy the code. Others might ask you to answer seven out of ten questions about the transmitted text or fill in missing words from the transmission. Even a multiple choice or true-false code examination is legal. The format of the telegraphy test is left to the discretion of the VE.

Disabled Hams

If you are sightless, without hearing or do not have use or control of your limbs, there are ways for you to transmit and receive ham radio communications and earn your Amateur Radio license. There is specialized equipment and volunteers to help you get started.

Volunteer Examiners can utilize special provisions when administering exams to handicapped applicants at the five-wpm level. These might include pauses after sentences, words or individual letters during the test. The examiners may require a physician's certification indicating the nature of the disability before deciding which, if any, special procedures should be used. If you have any disability, be sure to contact the Courage Handi-Ham System, Courage Center, 3915 Golden Valley Rd., Golden Valley, MN 55422, or call (612) 588-0811.

Pass Publications makes great Morse code learning and practice tapes. You can get their address from the photo.

Helping Hams

In virtually every area of the country there are Volunteer Examiners who want to help *you* join our hobby. At the National Amateur Radio Association, we call these people "Helping Hams." These Amateurs can advise you of local ham radio classes and, when the time comes, administer your Amateur test. The National Amateur Radio Association will assist you in locating people, Amateur clubs and organizations that will help you become a ham radio operator. Just call or write the National Amateur Radio Association for information.

Organizations To Contact

American Radio Relay League (ARRL). The premier national group representing radio Amateurs is the ARRL. Their address is: American Radio Relay League, 225 Main Street, Newington, Connecticut 06111, (203) 666-1541. Membership is currently $30.00 per year for United States residents and includes a subscription to their monthly publication, *QST* magazine.

National Amateur Radio Association (NARA). NARA is a special interest group. This non-profit organization was formed to: (a) publicize Amateur Radio to the general public; (b) bring young people into the hobby; (c) represent the interests of the Novice and Technician class Amateur and (d) protect Amateur frequency allocations. NARA can be reached in a number of ways.

National Amateur Radio Association
P.O. Box 598
Redmond, WA 98073-0598

Orders only- 1-(800) GOT-2-HAM
or 1-(800) 468-2426
MCI- NARANET1
CompuServe- 70371,111
Prodigy- MMVT95C
America Online- W6TNS DON

A membership in NARA is only $10.00 per year and includes a subscription to a bi-monthly member publication, *The Amateur Radio Communicator*.

Tucson Amateur Packet Radio (TAPR). Another special interest group is TAPR, PO Box 12925, Tucson, AZ 85732, (602) 749-9479. This group promotes packet radio communications via ham radio.

Amateur Satellite Corporation (AMSAT). AMSAT, 850 Sligo Avenue, Silver Spring, MD 20910, (301) 589-6062 is the amazing group that has parlayed memberships, donations and labor into more than 20 communication satellites that have orbited the earth exclusively for Amateur use.

Magazines are an excellent source of information no matter what field you are interested in. You can sometimes pick up copies of Amateur magazines on newsstands.

QST has something of interest for every ham with special emphasis on ARRL activities. Their address is ARRL, QST Magazine, 225 Main Street, Newington, CT 06111.

CQ's emphasis is on DX'ing, contesting and awards. They can be reached at CQ Magazine, 76 North Broadway, Hicksville, NY 11801.

73 is famed for its rich editorials by Wayne Green and for its emphasis on construction and articles for beginners. Write them at 73 Magazine, WGE Center, Hancock, NH 03449.

Amateur Communications (formerly *Radioscan* magazine) features many articles of interest to beginners. Their address is 8250 NW 27 St. #301, Miami, FL 33122.

For those interested in Amateur television transmissions, there are two excellent publications on the subject. One is *Amateur Television Quarterly*, 540 Oakton St., Des Plaines, IL 60018-1950. Drop a line to Henry Ruh, KB9FO if you would like a sample copy. *USATVS Journal* is published by Mike Donovan, KA0JAW. Mike has been reporting on ham TV for 22 years. They can be reached at USATVS, 1520 Cerro Dr., Dubuque, IA 52001.

An excellent publication for "homebrew artists" is called *Nuts & Volts* magazine. If you like to build things, or are interested in electronic parts and used equipment, you'll find what you are looking for between the covers of this publication. N&V covers not only ham things but television, test equipment and computer goodies. You can reach them by writing T & L Publications, Inc., P.O. Box 1111, Placentia, CA 92670. Tell them NARA sent you and watch for a sample copy in the mail.

If you would like to learn more about attaching your computer to an Amateur station, you will enjoy reading *Digital Digest*. It is the premier publication for the one's and zero's crowd and is only $16.00 per year. Digital Digest is published bimonthly by Arvo & Associates, 4063 Goldenrod Rd., Winter Park, FL 32792.

There are advertisements for a number of Amateur radio companies in these magazines. A letter to the advertiser requesting information will bring a quick response—usually a fat envelope full of literature.

These magazines provide an extraordinary amount of useful technical information. However, Amateur news is usually 60-90 days after the fact due to publishing deadlines. For the best up-to-date information on what's happening in the ham radio world, you should subscribe to the popular newsletters.

The most famous is the *W5YI Report*. This 10 page document is published by Fred Maia (W5YI) every two weeks and contains news which is never more than a few days old. The *W5YI Report* costs $24.50 per year and can be obtained by writing: The *W5YI Report*, P.O. Box 565101, Dallas, TX 75356-5101.

The oldest newsletter is *The Westlink Report*. It is published 26 times per year. It covers general Amateur radio news, FCC actions, new equipment releases, industry news, DX reports and propagation forecasts. The price is $24.50 per year. It's available from: Westlink Report, 28221 Stanley Ct., Canyon Country, CA 91351, telephone 1-(800) HAM-7303 or (805) 251-5558 in California.

There's a free service that provides the latest information on ham radio each week. It is the *Amateur Radio Newsline*, produced by Bill Pasternak (WA6ITF) and is heard weekly on repeaters all over the country. Check with your local repeater operator for the time "Newsline" can be heard. Or you can call the audio feed number at (805) 296-2407 to hear what the repeater operators tape record for later playback.

Let's Do It!

There's no shortage of information and there are no secrets. Come on and join us in this world of dits and dah's and ones and zeros. I can personally guarantee that your life will never again be the same. At the very least, you'll make new friends and have new experiences. Isn't that worth a few hours of your time?

73, DE Don Stoner, W6TNS
President
The National Amateur Radio Association

Chapter

The Birth Of A Hobby

Ｎone of the questions in the Novice or Technician test relate to the traditions of Amateurs. I think some of them should. These traditions are one of the things which separate Amateur Radio from other less disciplined services.

Hertz, The First Ham

Although we consider ham radio a twentieth-century hobby, the birth of an infant called "wireless" took place long before the turn of this century. In 1887, the chief interest of the population was attending band concerts in the park. That year, Heinrich Hertz, a brilliant young German scientist, was experimenting with the radiation of electricity. Hertz discovered that if he applied electricity to a loop of wire, he could cause a spark to jump the gap in another loop a short distance away — and with no connecting wires! This was the first form of radio communication.

Heinrich Hertz was the first person to generate radio waves. Was he the first ham?

Heinrich concluded correctly that electromagnetic waves traveled between the source gap and the spark gap at the speed of light. The source and the gap could be separated by only a few feet. At greater distances, the spark could not be detected.

Heinrich Hertz could be called the world's first Amateur. In appreciation and respect for his contribution, we have renamed the familiar unit of frequency to honor Hertz.

Today, instead of speaking of cycles, kilocycles or megacycles, we use the terms Hertz, kiloHertz and MegaHertz (Hz, kHz and MHz).

Morse Was an Artist

It's a little known fact, but Samuel Finley Breese Morse first achieved distinction as an artist, particularly as a painter of miniatures. He was the son of a Calvinist minister who was educated at Yale College and who received his art training in Europe. It was during the return voyage from Europe in 1832 that he devised the now famous code bearing his name.

Although well known for devising this system, he also invented the telegraphic sounder and printer. Both devices employed electromagnets, a battery and a telegraph key. Often the key was located a long distance from the electromagnets and connected by wires. This was the first telegraph line.

Morse connected the armature (controlled by the electromagnet) to an ink pen which could print on paper moving through the device. This created a printed record of the code. Using this scheme, the various alphanumeric characters of a message could be represented by combinations of the two signal elements, the "dot" and the "dash". For example, a "dot" followed by a "dash" represents an "A" in the international Morse code.

After working with the "printing telegraph", Morse and his colleague, Alfred Vail, realized that the messages could also be understood by *the sound of the clicking armature*. Holding the key down for a short length of time created a short click or "dot" sound while depressing the key longer increased the time before the next click. This represented a "dash".

The Morse code was utilized when radio telegraphy was introduced in 1897. Even submarines used the code by employing magnetic fields. Ships communicated between themselves using a signaling lamp wherein a shutter was manually actuated to form "dots" and "dashes".

Marconi—Wireless Pioneer

Guglielmo Marconi was the first to transmit signals across the Atlantic.

Apparently Hertz did not see the possibility of using electromagnetic waves for long distance communication. Guglielmo Marconi, an Italian genius, carried Hertz's simple experiment further by connecting one side of the "sending" spark gap to wires buried in the ground. The other side of the gap was connected to a "skywire" or antenna. Marconi utilized the telegraph code (devised by Samuel Morse for telegraph lines) with his new invention.

Rather than detecting a spark jumping a gap, Marconi used relatively sensitive detectors of electricity and headphones to permit hearing the sound of the spark signal.

Using this equipment, electromagnetic waves generated by the crackling spark traveled more than a mile to a remote receiving site. Transmitters, receivers and wireless communications had arrived on the scene; the year was 1895.

Marconi worked diligently to increase the range of communication. More sensitive devices were invented to reproduce the sound of the code. In time, practical distances reached 200 miles. Government and commercial companies all over the world copied Marconi's experiments and his wireless equipment. By the Fall of 1901, using a mighty spark gap transmitter, Marconi was able to thrust his signals 1,800 miles across the Atlantic Ocean from Wales to Newfoundland.

Litz Wire and Shellac

Cascading events and technological advances created more public interest in wireless communications than had ever been known. Experimenters found that they could listen in on this eighth wonder-of-the-world. They wound coils, varnished baseboards and built their own receiving stations. Interest in sending Morse code surged with the general population and Amateur transmitting stations sprang up all over the nation. Folks at the English end of the transatlantic circuit exhibited a similar interest. Their amateur experimenters were called "am's" and the name stuck for radio experimenters (it makes a good story, anyway!).

Keep in mind that there were no tubes, transistors, integrated circuits or even such basic items as capacitors, resistors or measuring meters. You couldn't go into a ham radio store and pick up a kit of parts. And there were no government regulations, frequency allocations, or organizations representing Amateurs. Anyone who wanted to experiment built the necessary parts and plunged into the construction of his or her Amateur station.

Snap, Crackle and Pop

Then the *rotary spark gap* was invented. Rather than use a fixed gap for the spark, this device used many gaps which rotated on a wheel at high speed. It produced pleasant sounding oscillations at the then fantastic rate of 50,000 cycles per second.

Even more important, the oscillations could be modified by the human voice! Reginald Aubrey Fessenden, a physicist, used speech to communicate with ships from his experimental station in Brant Rock, Mass. Many experimenters feared insanity when voices, rather than the whine of the rotary spark gap, leapt out of their headsets. But once again, Amateurs scrambled, this time to hurl their voices across space. The art of radiotelephone transmission had been created; the year was 1906.

Publications describing all kinds of devices for the experimenter were numerous. The papers described feats of distance and "heroism" by wireless stations almost daily.

The tiny stream of fire created by Hertz and Marconi had become a tremendous blaze in the eyes of experimenters everywhere.

With the increased activity came an ever-rising tide of interference between stations. Amateur, commercial and government activities were intermingled. The calliope of sounds culminated in the Wireless Act of 1912. This was the beginning of the rules which provide the framework under which Amateurs operate today. *The government was to control all wireless transmissions and all operators had to be licensed.*

The intrepid Amateurs, who sparked the imagination of commercial interests, were relegated to purgatory. Experiments showed that as the wavelength was decreased, the range of transmission was decreased. Since the long wavelengths (lower frequencies) were more valuable, they because the exclusive domain of commercial and government stations except by special permit. The operations of Amateurs had to be confined to the "useless" wavelengths shorter than 200 meters (near the high end of the present broadcast band).

The Amateur hobbyists protested violently, for they felt that this regulation effectively slashed the wrist of their sending hands. The new wavelengths were uninhabited and incapable of propagating energy across a small village, *or so they thought.* The more progressive experimenters soon discovered that their range had been increased, rather than decreased, and with no additional transmitting power! The better stations could communicate over distances in excess of 30 miles.

Formation Of The ARRL

In 1914 another great event occurred. The Radio Club of Hartford, Conn., formed a league of Amateur stations. This group, known as the American Radio Relay League, still represents it's members in all official matters. The purpose of the League was to band Amateurs together so they could relay messages from one point to another (as commercial stations did) so that individual stations could communicate beyond the 30 mile limit.

An early network of Amateurs was attempted between Boston and Denver, with the eventual hope of spanning the continent. Soon, with the leadership of League co-founder Hiram Percy Maxim, messages were flying back and forth. By 1921, with improved equipment and techniques, a message and answer could make the round trip between coasts in six minutes!

Hiram Percy Maxim, co-founder of the American Radio Relay League. (ARRL photo

Although the League suffered financial troubles, it was able to publish the first issue of its official organ in December, 1915 — a magazine still known as "*QST*".

During the First World War, two-thirds of the 6,000 Amateurs trooped off to the battlefield, and all Amateur transmissions ceased. During the war, and with the help of Amateurs, the government discovered how valuable the wavelengths shorter than 200 meters were. These frequencies became the exclusive property of the Navy and after the shooting had died down, the Navy was hesitant to return them. Under the pressure of League president Maxim and secretary Warner, however, the government relented. In October of 1919, Amateur operation was restored. Call letters, consisting of *a number and two letters*, were again assigned, based on area, to Amateurs. (It was much later before the A, K, N and W prefixes were added).

The Magic Bottle

The war also made a commercial item out of a device that was once a laboratory curiosity. In 1905, Sir Ambrose Fleming invented the diode "valve". It consisted of a filament and plate inside an evacuated bulb. Current would only flow from filament to plate and not the other way around. Thus, it could be used to convert alternating into direct current.

In 1907, Dr. Lee DeForest installed a grid between the filament and the plate. He found that by varying the voltage on the grid, he could control the current flow between the filament and the plate. More important, only a small change of voltage on the grid would result in a large voltage change at the plate. This is called **amplification**. The device was patented as the "Audion" or triode vacuum tube.

Because of amplification, this "magic bottle" could be used to make receivers more sensitive. Even more important, the vacuum tube could be used to generate radio signals electronically, with no moving parts like the rotary spark gap. Suddenly, generating stable radio frequency energy became possible. Further, the human voice could now be transmitted over the airwaves in channels much narrower than with the spark gap.

The glow of the vacuum tube filament cast a shadow over the spark gap and helix coil which signaled the end of a great era. With a mighty whoosh of ozone, King Spark sputtered and died!

New Vistas

Armed with this new electronic invention (the vacuum tube), the ARRL sent Paul F. Godly, 2ZE, to Europe for transatlantic tests. Keep in mind that "conventional wisdom" at the time was that as distance increased, radio signals got weaker until they could no longer be detected. What a revelation it must have been to discover that the same signals **once again reappear** at great distances from the point of origin. With this knowledge, the science of **radio progagation** (see *Chapter 3*) was born and the high frequency bands suddenly became *very valuable for long distance communications*.

Radio station F8AB in France was the first to work an American Amateur Radio station.

During the transatlantic experiments, thirty American Amateurs were heard on the continent. Finally, after many months of preparation, the first two-way Amateur contact flashed across the Atlantic.

In the course of these tests, it was discovered that *the shorter wavelengths provided superior propagation* of electromagnetic energy. Later it was found that the wavelengths between *40 and 10 meters* were optimum for long distance contacts. A mass exodus to the "short wavelength" bands began which made the California Gold Rush seem like a school fire drill. Further, Amateurs found that their ability to communicate over long distances was affected by the time of year and a strange, new cycle which seemed to be influenced by the sun.

An American Inventor

The inventions of Major Edwin Armstrong will forever shape and influence ham radio. In 1918, he discovered the principal of *heterodyning* and invented the *superheterodyne receiver.*

Until Armstrong's invention, it was necessary to peak each amplifier stage in a radio receiver individually. The receivers were called tuned radio frequency or TRF receivers. This peaking was an awkward operation. Some designers tried to tie the knobs of the various stages together, but it was virtually impossible to obtain perfect tracking between all the tuned circuits.

Major Armstrong discovered that the amplifying circuits of a radio could all be tuned to a single frequency. Using the heterodyne principal, the desired station could be converted to this single frequency for processing. All modern radios and television receivers employ this superheterodyne principle.

Equally important was Armstrong's invention of frequency modulation. Prior to 1937, voice was broadcast by varying the amplitude or strength of the electromagnetic waves radiated by the antenna. Armstrong discovered that voice information could also be conveyed by varying the frequency of the electromagnetic waves, rather than the amplitude. Since static and electrical interference varies in amplitude but not frequency, noise can be completely filtered out in a frequency modulation receiver. Thanks to Armstrong, you hear high fidelity, static free reception on the FM band, not to mention the VHF ham bands.

This early era in the development of radio communications is chronicled in an interesting videotape called Empire Of The Air. It is based on the PBS broadcast which described the competitive relationships between Dr. DeForest, Major Edwin Armstrong and David Sarnoff, who headed the Radio Corporation of America (RCA) and the National Broadcasting Company (NBC). Empire Of The Air can be obtained at many video rental stores and is well worth your effort to locate it.

The Single Sideband Mode

As you might suspect, spark gap transmissions were not very efficient. Each transmitter consumed more radio spectrum "real estate" than does an entire Amateur band today! The vacuum tube made narrow channel amplitude modulation possible. But with the passage of time a new technology made AM obsolete. The technique was called *single sideband, suppressed carrier* or simply *SSB*.

Single sideband is not a recent invention. It has been around for longer than most people reading this book. The telephone company has used single sideband since the '30's in order to squeeze more channels into their telephone circuits.

It took the Strategic Air Command (SAC) and the "cold war" of the '50's and '60's to bring single sideband out of the closet. General "Butch" Griswold and Curtis LeMay, working in conjunction with Arthur Collins, W0CXX, of the Collins Radio Company, developed an extraordinary communications network using conventional Amateur single sideband equipment. The network permitted reliable communications with SAC sideband equipped airplanes and SAC bases all over the world at any time of the day or night.

Amateurs like Wes Schum and Herb Johnson adapted the SSB technique to popularly priced ham gear. When this happened, the mass exodus from "Ancient Mary" (Amplitude Modulation) to single sideband was underway on the ham bands.

The transition was not painless, however. "Sidebanders" huddled at one end of the 20 and 75 meter ham bands, while the "AM'ers" reigned supreme in the remainder of

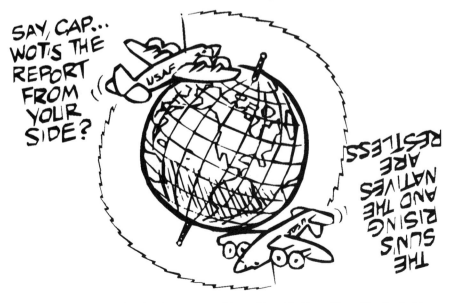

the bands. Slowly, but inexorably, the ranks of those operating SSB expanded. Invariably they interfered with diehard "AM'ers". The SSB "static" a ham heard on their AM receiver was very annoying. But the benefits afforded by SSB could not be denied. Over time, most "AM'ers" either died off or converted to SSB.

For communications, AM (like spark) is a relic of the past. It is still used on the Citizens Band. In commercial service, only the Aeronautical Service still uses AM for communication between planes and to the control tower at airports. Actually there is an advantage to AM in aeronautical applications. When the tower is listening to a pilot and hears a "whistle," they know that someone else is calling them. With FM or SSB there would be no audible heterodyne and the tower might miss the calls of weaker stations.

Not only is SSB an *extremely efficient use of spectrum* but it packs a lot of communication "punch" per watt of power. Want to see the hair on the neck of an ole time CW man stand straight out? Just make the statement, at your next club meeting, that SSB will "get through" anytime that CW can also be received! Most "sidebanders" believe that it will, but the subject is always good for a lively debate.

If you earn a Novice or Tech-Plus license, you can operate SSB voice on the 10-meter band. When radio propagation conditions are optimum, you will be able to talk with other Amateurs around the world!

Ham Radio — Out Of This World

Today, with modern technology, we think nothing of speaking with Amateurs on the other side of the globe—it happens daily! In fact, the Amateur Service has literally soared through the ionosphere and far out into space.

The introduction of satellite communication certainly ranks as one of the major accomplishments of Amateurs. In 1959, I suggested in the April *CQ* Magazine the possibility of putting an Amateur station in orbit. The concept was picked up by a group of Amateurs who worked for a major aerospace company. The idea grew to become the **OSCAR (Orbital Satellite Carrying Amateur Radio)** program.

You can buy hardware and software to display space photos on your computer. (AEA Photo)

Their initial effort culminated in a shoebox-sized satellite which held a tiny transmitter and whip antenna. It was keyed electronically and beeped the Morse code letters for the Amateur greeting (HI) from space.

OSCAR One was launched on December 12, 1961. Amateurs around the world were thrilled to hear their representative "speaking" from the cosmos.

If you would like to hear what the first OSCAR satellite sounded like, the National Amateur Radio Association sells a tape called *The Flight of OSCAR One*. It was recorded at Vandenberg AFB in 1961. Also captured are transmissions on the 40-meter OSCAR net along with reception of the HI beacon of the satellite at various stages of its life. The tape can be ordered from NARA and is priced at $4.95 postage paid.

Today, we Amateurs have sophisticated repeater satellites which are capable of worldwide communications. Some of the OSCAR satellites follow eliptical orbits with an apogee (the furthest point from the earth) of 35,000 kilometers. The satellite "hangs" near the apogee for several hours. From this high point, it "sees" half the surface of the earth. Thus you can communicate for long distances (not only up and down, but across the earth) transmitting via OSCAR. And you can do this with a Technician license since the satellites operate on VHF and UHF bands.

There are also low earth orbit Amateur Radio satellites that circle the earth every 90 minutes or so. You can hitch your computer to a ham rig via a device similar to a modem and commuicate via sattelite. These OSCARs store and forward digital messages. Just think, you can file a message on an OSCAR and 45 minutes later, a ham in Japan can off-load the message from the orbiting mailbox. You only need a Technician license to be qualified to do this.

Ham satellites are all the more amazing when one considers that not only are they free to use, but they were built with contributed labor and are launched through private enterprise without government assistance. The organization responsible for these technological miracles is called AMSAT-NA, The Amateur Satellite Corporation for North America (*see Introduction Chapter*).

Computer Communications

Another event which forever changed the face of ham radio was the introduction of computer **packet** communications. Until recently, clattering, oil spewing Teletype(tm) machines were the closest thing hams had to digital communication. Packet is a fast and error-free method of communicating with computers.

The "sparkplug" of Amateur packet communications was Dr. John D. Mercado of the Canadian Department of Communications. In addition to introducing the *Digital Certificate of Proficiency* license in Canada, he inspired the Vancouver Amateur Digital Communications Group to develop a packet controller. The Vancouver club developed a device called a **Terminal Node Controller (TNC)**. It is similar to a computer modem but optimized for the one-way-at-a-time communications of ham radio. It also has built-in error correction so that received data is always an accurate reproduction of what was originally sent.

In the early '80's, a group of Amateurs in Tucson, Arizona took the concept one step further. The Tucson Amateur Packet Radio (TAPR) organization "tweeked" and simplified the Vancouver design. They built kits and licensed the new TNC design to manufacturers. As a result, most packet TNC's sold today are based on this famous TAPR design (*see Introduction Chapter*).

Continue The Traditions

While this "thumb-nail" sketch is by no means complete, it should convey to you some of the important history and tradition behind our fantastic hobby. Those who join us are expected to respect the traditions of Amateurs, to appreciate the loan of valuable spectrum and to maintain our high standards. Now, let's get to work and study for the Technician examination.

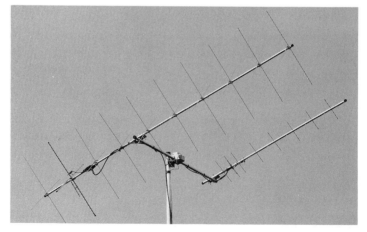

The AOP-1 is a typical antenna system for working VHF and UHF Amateur satellites.

Chapter

The FCC Rules and Regulations

This section of your test will include 10 questions from the Novice question pool (Element 2) and 5 questions from the Technician pool (Element 3A). At the end of various paragraphs, in this and following chapters, you will note mysterious characters in parenthesis. These refer to the question pool numbers. The questions for the chapter subject are located at the end of each chapter. All questions from the Novice pool are preceded with an "N" while those from the Technician pool are preceded with a "T".

If you are sure you understand an explanation, you can mentally and visually skip over these numbers and go on to the next paragraph. If your understanding is a bit hazy, look up the question at the end of each chapter and try to answer it based on what you learned in the paragraph.

It's now time for the "main event!" The preceding two chapters were just the "prelims." In this corner, wearing the mauve trunks with the brocade trim is the Federal Communications Commission. And in the opposite corner, bouncing from foot-to-foot and throwing practice jabs, is "Prospective-Tech" (that's you). Proceed fearlessly, "Prospective-Tech," everyone is pulling for you to win this bout, including the FCC.

The Rules of the Road

There's not much exciting about rules and regulations unless you happen to break one! However, you'll need to know about the "rules of the road" in order to pass your Amateur Radio license test. Almost a third of the 55 questions you'll be asked will involve the regulations under which we all operate.

Virtually all transmitting stations are regulated through rules established by the Federal Communications Commission (FCC). Amateurs operate under the **Amateur Service** in **Part 97 of title 47 CFR (Code of Federal Regulations)** of these rules. Part 97 is the section which establishes the rules for the Amateur Service. If you would like to study Part 97 in depth, a booklet containing the rules can be obtained from The National Amateur Radio Association for $5.00 postage paid. (N1A01)(N1A02)

Why Have An Amateur Radio Service?

Amateur communication is defined as **non-commercial communications between Amateur stations, for pleasure and not for compensation**. The Amateur Service is a radio communications service for the purpose of *self-training* in communications and *technical investigations*. An Amateur station is a combination of equipment used in the Amateur Radio Service for radio communications. The rules in Part 97 discuss such things as station *operating standards, technical standards and emergency communications*. (N1A03)(N1A04)(N1A08)(N1A09)

There are five principles that guide the Amateur Service. They are (1) recognition of emergency communications; (2) advancement of the radio art; (3) improvement of communication and technical skills; (4) increase the number of trained radio operators and electronics experts; and (5) the enhancement of international goodwill. *Etch these five principles into your brain*. You will be asked about this in the Element 2 questions. (N1A05)(N1A06)

Who can earn an Amateur license and become a ham? Almost *anyone of any age*, size or shape, even if they are not a citizen of this country. There are even Russians who hold a valid American Amateur Radio license. In fact, the only people who are specifically precluded from holding a United States Amateur license are *representatives of a foreign government*. (N1D01)(N1D02)

The FCC allows aliens to operate Amateur stations in the United States if they hold a reciprocal permit from the FCC, or Canadians who hold an Amateur Service license from the Government of Canada. (N1B07)

Your Ticket To The World

One of the factors which distinguishes the Amateur Service from the Citizens Band is the **Amateur license**. This document, sometimes referred to as a "ticket" by hams, is issued by the Federal Communications Commission and allows you to operate an Amateur station and transmit on Amateur Service frequencies. (N1B01)(N1B03)

Let's talk a bit about the ham license. You could be asked several questions based on it when you take the Technician test.

OK, Who's In Charge Here?

The answer, in a single word, is **you**. Any licensed Amateur should have total control of his or her Amateur station. You, as the licensed Amateur in charge, are called the **control operator**. The **control point** is the location at which the control operator function is performed. By the way, you must always have your Amateur license (or a photocopy) in your possession whenever you are operating an Amateur Station. The

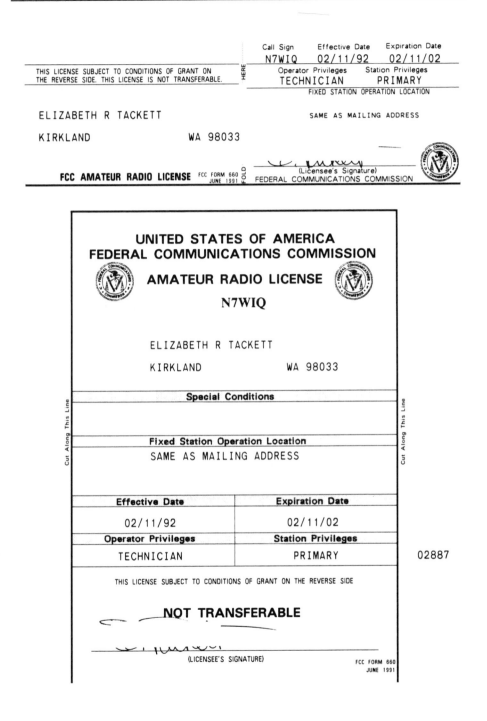

	Call Sign	Effective Date	Expiration Date
THIS LICENSE SUBJECT TO CONDITIONS OF GRANT ON THE REVERSE SIDE. THIS LICENSE IS NOT TRANSFERABLE.	N7WIQ	02/11/92	02/11/02
	Operator Privileges	Station Privileges	
	TECHNICIAN	PRIMARY	

FIXED STATION OPERATION LOCATION

ELIZABETH R TACKETT   SAME AS MAILING ADDRESS

KIRKLAND   WA 98033

FCC AMATEUR RADIO LICENSE FCC FORM 660 JUNE 1991

(Licensee's Signature)
FEDERAL COMMUNICATIONS COMMISSION

UNITED STATES OF AMERICA
FEDERAL COMMUNICATIONS COMMISSION
AMATEUR RADIO LICENSE
N7WIQ

ELIZABETH R TACKETT

KIRKLAND   WA 98033

Special Conditions

Fixed Station Operation Location
SAME AS MAILING ADDRESS

Effective Date	Expiration Date
02/11/92	02/11/02
Operator Privileges	**Station Privileges**
TECHNICIAN	PRIMARY

02887

THIS LICENSE SUBJECT TO CONDITIONS OF GRANT ON THE REVERSE SIDE

NOT TRANSFERABLE

(LICENSEE'S SIGNATURE)

FCC FORM 660
JUNE 1991

The new style of Amateur Radio license from the Federal Communication Commission comes in two parts, one which you carry and the other for posting in the Amateur station.

license (or a photocopy) must also be retained at the station. (N1B06)(N1B10) (N1G05)(N1G11)(T1A01)(T1A02)

As the station licensee and control operator, you are held responsible for the proper operation of your station *whenever it is transmitting*. Any Amateur station must have a licensed control operator present at the control point whenever transmitting (unless it is remote controlled). If you let an unlicensed person talk on your station, you must continuously monitor and supervise the person's participation. Whatever happens in your station, you are always held accountable by the FCC. (N1G09)(N1G10)(T1E09)

If you *let another Amateur use your station*, they are considered to be the *control operator*. If they have a higher operating class, they may use their privileges on your equipment. By the same token, if you use a station of someone with a higher operating class, you still must operate in accordance with the privileges of your license class. (N1G01)(N1G08)

However, if either party uses the other person's station improperly, you are held *equally responsible* with the other person. You cannot permit an unlicensed person to use your station without your supervision. (N1G02)(N1G03)(N1G04)(N1G06) (N1G07)

The FCC authorization really consists of two licenses on a single piece of paper. One part of the document conveys operator privileges. This is the **operator license** and, as the name implies, *permits you to control an Amateur station*. An Amateur station consists of the apparatus necessary for carrying on radio communications. (N1B02)

As a newly licensed Amateur, the document the government sends you also provides a **station license**. This portion of the license permits you to have an Amateur station. The address on your ham license is the current and accurate mailing address. This is where you receive correspondence and where the FCC can communicate with you, if they need to. (N1D04)

The Amateur operator named by the license has a written authorization to be the **control operator** of an Amateur station. He or she is held responsible for the correct operation of an Amateur station. (N1A07)(N1A10)

More About That "Ticket"

The holder of an FCC Amateur license is permitted to operate an Amateur station anywhere that the Amateur Service is regulated by the Federal Communications Commission. (N1B04)

Your Amateur license is *good for the period specified on the license*, which is currently *10 years* from the date of issue. If your license expires and you forget to renew it, you have a *two year grace period* to do so. However, try to renew not later than 60 to 90 days after expiration, at the very latest. If you wait longer than this, it makes extra work for the FCC personnel. Renewal or modification of your license is simply a matter of filling out an FCC Form 610 and sending it to the Federal Communications Commission, P.O. Box 1020, Gettysburg, PA 17326. **Don't forget to attach a copy of your current license**. If your license is lost or destroyed, you can request a duplicate by writing the FCC in Gettysburg and explaining what happened to your license. (N1D05)(N1D06)(N1D10)(N1D11)(T1A03)(T1A04)

Give Me A Sign

There is a third component to the Amateur license. It is your **station identification** or call sign. When you are granted a license, you also receive a distinct set of alphanumeric characters which constitutes your *station call letters*. All calls have a minimum of four alphanumeric characters and a maximum of six. Amateur Extra class hams are issued the shorter calls. The call letters of US Amateur stations begin with the letters A, K, N or W. The group can be 2 by 1 (WX7S), 1 by 2 (K6DC), 1 by 3 (N7NQL), 2 by 2 (AC7XY) or 2 by 3 (KB7GIS). There are no 1 by 1 calls. The digits can be any number, zero through nine. The numbers represent certain geographic areas of the country. For example all California or Hawaii licensees are issued number six designators. (N1D07)(N1D08)(N1D09)

As a brand new Amateur, your call letters will be from the 1 by 3 (Group C) or 2 by 3 (Group D) variety. Novice operators are always issued Group D format callsigns. Technicians usually get Group C (1 by 3) call signs starting with the letter "N." Technicians receive Group D (2 by 3) callsigns when all of the "N" prefixed 1 by 3 callsigns are allocated in a specific radio district.

Your call sign is unique. *No one else in the world has one like it*. You should be proud of what it represents—the license you have earned. Always use your call properly

Students studying for the Technician test in the Gordon West (WB6NOA) Radio School. The "pass" ribbons are a big hit with students. Photo by Martha Lostrom, KA1UUO.

and with pride. You must identify your station with the call sign at the **end** of each transmission series and every 10 minutes in an extended conversation. In other words, you need not give your call after you say "Hi Joe, how's the weather in Moosejaw?" or when Joe says "It's a bit cold and overcast". After 10 minutes of this chit-chatting, however, you must identify. No matter when you end the conversation, you must also identify your station. It is the responsibility of the person you are talking to, to identify his or her station. (N1H06)(N1H07)(N1H08)(N1H09)(N1H11)

Go To The Head Of The Class

There are five United States Amateur operator license classes. They are, in order of increasing privileges: Novice, Technician, General, Advanced and Amateur Extra. There are two beginner or "entry level" paths. These are the **Novice** and the **Technician class** license. The latter requires no knowledge of Morse code as discussed in the *Introduction* chapter. (N1B08)(N1B09)(N1B11)

Novice—The basic path for beginners is called the **Novice class**. Many young people prefer this license class to the Technician class. Novices are required to learn to receive Morse code at the 5-WPM level (Element 1A) but the theory test (Element 2) is less extensive that the Technician Test.

This Novice class was also described in the *Introduction* Chapter. It allows Morse code operation on the high frequency (HF) bands, plus voice communications on 10 meters. (N1D03)

Technician—The written tests for the Technician class license are officially designated Element 2 and Element 3(A) by the FCC. Element 2 consists of 30 questions from the Novice question pool. Element 3(A) is made up of 25 questions from the Technician question pool. Both tests consist of multiple choice questions on elementary theory, Amateur practices and basic FCC regulations.

Technician-Plus—A step up the ham radio ladder is a license class commonly called the **Technician Plus**. To reach this level you must pass a five word-per-minute Morse code test, called Element 1(A), in addition to earning your Technician license. (T1A10)

By the way, "Technician Plus" is not an official FCC term but it has been popularly adopted by the Amateur community to mean a Tech who has also passed the Morse code test. You may also hear the informal term "Tech-Lite." The term is not derrogatory, but is a slightly chiding reference which means someone who has not yet passed the Morse code test, Element 1(A).

The Element 1(A) test is conducted in a VE session when other written tests are given. Once it is established that you have passed Element 1(A), you receive a *Certificate of Successful Completion of Examination (CSCE)* from the examiners. At this point you become a Technician Plus and you are allowed to immediately operate on certain long distance high frequency bands below 30 MHz. (T1A11)

Examinees who have upgraded are permitted to *immediately* utilize their new operating privileges. They must, however, append their call signs with an identifier to denote that they have not yet received their new license. The identifier for Technician who has upgraded to Technician Plus can be any word to represet the slant bar, followed by the letters KT. A chart of temporary appended upgrading identifiers is shown below. (T1C01)

UPGRADE TO:	CW IDENTIFICATION	VOICE IDENTIFICATION
Technician Plus	Your call/KT	Your call/temporary KT
General	Your call/AG	Your call/temporary AG
Advanced	Your call/AA	Your call/temporory AA
Amateur Extra	Your call/AE	Your call/temporory AE

General—Most Amateurs aspire to become **General class** hams because it allows worldwide communications on the most popular high frequency (HF) bands. The written test for the General class license (Element 3B) is about the same difficulty as for the Technician Element 3(A) test. However, the general theory questions emphasize operating on bands to which the General class ham has access. The Morse code requirements are increased to 13 WPM. This class of license provides access to all of the Amateur bands, but not all parts of them.

Advanced And Amateur Extra—The next higher class is called the **Advanced class,** while the top of the pyramid is called the **Amateur Extra**. These licenses provide a few more privileges and total access to the Amateur bands.

Remember these five classes of license—Novice, Technician, General, Advanced and Amateur Extra.

Can You See The Radio Spectrum?

In order to understand the Amateur bands and the frequencies we use, it helps to visualize the radio spectrum. You will have to learn what parts of this spectrum Amateurs are allowed to use. These are the bands that the FCC has allocated for Amateur operation.

Imagine for a moment that you are standing on a high plateau of land overlooking a vast panorama in front of you. From off in the distance, to your far left, you hear the faint sounds of Motley Crue flogging their guitars to death. These are the sound frequencies with an address of 0 to .02.

Clockwise from that location, you can see numerous airplanes converging. This is the land where the aeronautical navigation beacons are located at addresses between 0.2 and 0.5.

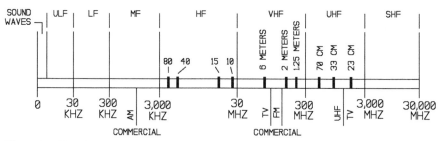

Figure 1-1 This drawing shows the relative "location" of various services throughout the radio spectrum.

Next to this is a forest of tall steel towers supported by guy wires. These are the antennas of the AM broadcast band stations. The address of these stations is between 0.5 and 1.5.

Then, arrayed in front of you are numerous towers, boats with antennas and aircraft with wires from wing tip to tail. Sprinkled among them are wires stretched between trees, and Amateur antenna systems looking like TV antennas with an overactive thyroid. This conglomeration is the high frequency band which occupies the real estate address between 3.0 and 30.

Off to your right is another forest of tall towers and buildings which represent the FM and television broadcasting stations. Again, nestled in the shadow of these monsters, are another group of antennas representing the Amateur Radio inhabitants in the land between 30 and 300. There are more huge antennas to the right owned by the UHF television stations between 500 and 800.

Off in the distance to the far right are literally millions of automobiles all with tiny tails raised in anticipation from their rear windows. A closer inspection reveals drivers in animated conversation. This is the land of the cellular telephone which has an address of approximately 800 to 900.

Next to these automobiles are almost an equal number of shiny aluminum dishes pointed skyward. These are the satellite receiving and sending terminal antenna systems. They are planted on real estate labeled 1,000 and up.

Finally, off to the extreme right is a bright illumination representing the visible light spectrum. Although you can't see the emissions, invisible tanning as well as infrared rays are being radiated from the same general area.

The panorama just described is an overview of the radio communications spectrum, and is illustrated in *Figure 1-1*. The "address" referred to is the frequency in millions of cycles per second. A million cycles is the same as one megaHertz (MHz). So that you can better visualize emissions, you may want to take a "side trip" to *Chapter 3*, at this point.

With this general picture of the radio spectrum in mind, let's examine the various bands that you are allowed to utilize as a Technician class Amateur.

Meters And Megs

So far, I've spoken of the radio spectrum in terms of both meters and megaHertz. The relationship between the two will remain a deep-dark secret unless you take a break at this point and peek at the beginning of *Chapter 3*.

At this point, I will tell you about a very special number that allows you to convert from one to the other. It is the number **300** and is called a *constant*. Remember it and you won't go wrong on your test. Simply divide megaHertz (MHz) into 300 and the answer is in meters—or the other way around. Got that—300?

For example, convert 80 meters to a corresponding frequency. Divide 80 into 300 and the answer is 3.75 (MHz). Think you have it? What is 30 MHz in meters?

The High Frequency Amateur Bands

The accompanying charts, *Figures 1-2* and *1-3*, show the radio spectrum and where the popular Amateur bands are located. Although Technician class Amateurs are permitted all operating privileges above 30 MHz, they are not allowed to operate on the high frequency (HF) bands. *The HF band is the frequency spectrum between 3.0 and 30.0 MHz.* The International Telecommunications Union (ITU), requires a knowledge of Morse code for operation on the high frequency bands.

Technicians can access the high frequency bands by taking a five word-per-minute Morse test called Element 1(A). Passing this test reclassifies them as Technician Plus (plus Morse). Novice high frequency operation is permitted since this class of Amateur has passed the Element 1(A) Morse test to earn the license.

Novice and Technician Plus operators are permitted a maximum transmitter output of 200 watts peak envelope power on the high frequency bands (3-30 MHz) on which they are authorized to operate. Even so, one should always use the minimum legal power necessary to carry out the desired communications. (N1F01)(N1F02)(N1F03)(N1F04)(N1F05)(N1F06)(N1F09)

The following is a brief discussion of the characteristics of the high frequency Amateur bands.

80 Meters—The entire band extends from 3.5 to 4.0 MHz (3500 to 4000 kHz). Novice and Tech-Plus hams are permitted to operate between **3675 and 3725 kHz (3.675 to 3.725 MHz)** within this band. Operation is strictly by Morse code, or continuous wave (CW) as it is more correctly called. *No phone operation by Novices is permitted.* You can usually communicate up to 50-75 miles during the day and 400 miles or more at night. (N1C01)(N1C07)(N1E01)(N1E04)

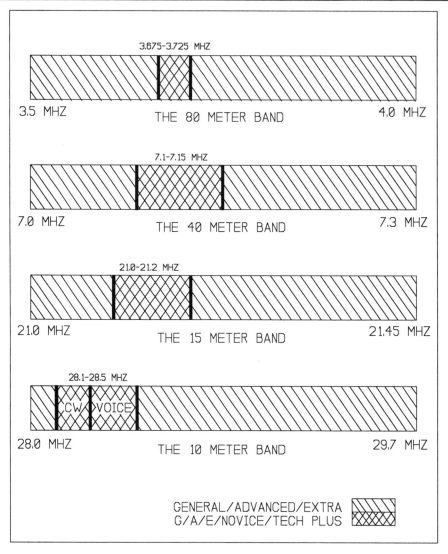

Figure 1-2 Popular HF bands, showing Novice and Tech-Plus allocations.

40 Meters—This is the favorite CW band (code emission only) of Novices and Tech-Plus operators. They are permitted to operate between **7100 and 7150 kHz (7.1 to 7.15 MHz)**. During the day you can expect to "talk" with other hams around 300 miles distance. *At night it's possible to work all over the United States.* If the foreign short-wave broadcast interference is not too great, don't be surprised if someone from overseas answers your CQ (I'd like to communicate with someone) call. (N1C02)(N1C08)(N1E02)(N1E05)

15 Meters—This is another CW emission only band (for beginners) which permits worldwide communications, but mostly in the daytime. At night the band is usually dead (except during solar peaks every 11 years). Novice and Tech-Plus hams are permitted to thump away on their telegraph keys between 21.100 and 21.200 MHz (what is that in kiloHertz?). (N1C03)(N1C09)(N1E03)(N1E06)(T1A05)

10 Meters—During periods of high solar activity one can communicate all over the world on 10 meters. It is also the only Novice and Tech-Plus HF band where *phone communication is permitted*. The full band is 28.0 to 29.7 MHz. Novice and Tech-Plus hams are permitted CW, RTTY and digital operation between 28.100 and 28.300 MHz. Between 28.3 and 28.5 MHz Novice and Tech-Plus Amateurs can operate CW and phone. This is the only HF band on which phone operation is permitted by beginning class Amateurs. (N1C04)(N1C10)(N1E07)(N1E08)(N1E11)(N1E13)(N1E14)

There are several other small Amateur allocations within the HF spectrum, but a General class or higher license is required to access them.

The VHF And UHF Amateur Bands

The most popular bands are located in the portion of the radio spectrum called **Very High Frequencies (VHF)**. The VHF bands are located between 30 and 300 MHz. Between 300 and 3,000 MHz, the spectrum is referred to as the **Ultra High Frequencies (UHF)**. The majority of Amateur operation on VHF and UHF is voice, using the frequency modulation (FM) mode.

These are called **line-of-sight** frequencies since VHF (and higher) radio transmissions don't bend (except under unusual circumstances). Thus, *these frequencies are not capable of following the curvature of the earth*. As a result you can expect to talk 20 miles or so directly, or up to 100 miles via a VHF repeater. Then these "straight line" transmissions head for the cold eternity of space.

Six Meters—This is the lowest frequency VHF band on which the Technician class Amateur is allowed to operate. The band extends from 50 to 54 MHz. All Amateur classes, *except Novice*, can operate on the six meter band. The band from 50.0 to 50.1 is reserved exclusively for CW. Thus, frequency modulation (FM) can *only be used from 50.1 to 54.0 MHz*. The only other prohibition is that stations on this band may not be used for satellite communications. (T1A06)(1B08)(T1B11)

The six meter band is rather unusual from a number of standpoints. For many years six meters was shunned because of television interference. It is "located" right next to Channel 2 in the radio spectrum (Channel 2 occupies frequencies between 54 and 60 Mhz.). Because of proximity, a six meter transmitter can interfere with a nearby television receiver through no fault of the ham gear or the Amateur. However, try explaining that to an irate neighbor when *Wheel of Fortune* is getting "creamed!"

Television set designs have improved and they are now better able to reject unwanted signals. More importantly, cable television is starting to dominate the landscape. It is highly unlikely that a six meter transmitter would interfere with Channel 2 on a television connected to cable since the signal is enclosed in a shielded coaxial line.

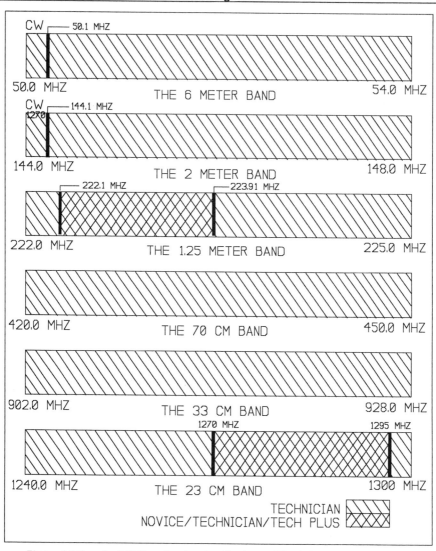

Figure 1-3 Popular VHF bands, showing Novice and Tech-Plus allocations.

Six is an excellent band for around-town communication with a simple low power transmitter. Occasionally, when the sun decides to act up (see *Chapter 3*), it is possible to communicate with foreign countries. It is not unusual to tune across a "dead" band and hear a single station coming in from Buenos Aires, Argentina, in South America!

Two Meters—The favorite of the Technician class is the two meter band, which occupies 144 to 148 Mhz. The majority of people operating VHF will be found on "two." Like six meters, *Novice operation is not permitted* but all other Amateur classes may use the band. The maximum transmitting power permitted an Amateur station is 1,500 watts peak envelope power (PEP). Note that the band between 144.0 and 144.1

is reserved exclusively for CW. Thus, emissions other than CW can *only be used between 144.1 and 148.0 MHz*. (T1A07)(T1B09)

Most repeaters operate on two meters. Many of the orbital satellites carrying Amateur Radio (OSCAR), as well as several of the Russian satellites, receive two-meter signals. Computer communication (*packet*) is concentrated on two meters.

1.25 Meters—Technicians are permitted to operate on the entire band between 222 and 225 MHz. All Amateur modes and emissions are authorized for the Technician and higher license classes. Novices are only permitted operation between *222.1 and 223.91 MHz and are restricted to a transmitter power of 25 watts or less*. (N1C05)(N1C11)(N1E09)(N1E12)(N1F07)(N1F10)(T1A08)

70 Centimeters—This is an interesting band for the experimenter. The band limits are 420-450 MHz and there are some operating restrictions near the Canadian border and adjacent to military reservations. *No Novice operation is permitted*, but all other classes may use 70 centimeters. (T1A09)

Most of the present Amateur television (ATV) transmissions occur within this band. Hams in some of the larger cities have even installed television repeaters. Many of the voice repeaters operating on this band belong to clubs and are closed to non-members.

33 Centimeters—There is a little known Amateur frequency allocation between 902 and 928 MHz. It is shared with a number of unlicensed services such as vehicle locators, video links for VCR's and wireless data links. It is likely that Amateur activity or interest in this band will further decrease as commercial use increases. There are no questions in the test pool relating to the 33 cm. band.

23 Centimeters—This band, which extends from 1240 to 1300 MHz is getting more popular as crowding increases on the lower VHF bands. New repeaters are regularly heard as more commercial equipment becomes available.

There is much more "real estate" for Amateur television transmissions. It is likely that most ATV operation will move up to 23 cm. Even though the wavelength is very short, the performance of equipment is excellent. Signals are more susceptible to reflection. Thus, 23 cm. transmissions seem to bounce into areas that are not penetrated by lower band VHF signals.

Technicians are allowed to operate on any frequency within the band. *Novices are restricted to the portion between 1270 and 1295 MHz*. All emissions authorized for this band may be used but transmitting output for Novices is restricted to 5 watts peak envelope power (PEP). (N1C06)(N1E10)(N1F07)(N1F11)

There are several micro wavelength Amateur bands higher in frequency than the ones just discussed and Technician class Amateurs can use them all. These bands will become increasingly popular as Amateur satellite activity multiplies.

Where Am I?

There are no geographical limitations on the use of your ham license within the United States or on the high seas. You can operate wherever you want, in areas where the FCC has jurisdiction, without notifying the FCC. You can also operate your station in foreign countries if they have reciprocal licensing agreements with the United States. If you are operating aboard a boat in the territorial waters of another country, you should check with the local authorities on the status of reciprocal licensing agreements. (N1H01)

Many years ago, the address on your license was where the FCC expected to find your station. If you operated at another location you were supposed to advise the FCC Engineer-in-Charge for your radio district. This requirement was abandoned when vehicular radio operation and our mobile society flooded them with unnecessary paperwork.

Verboten Countries

From time-to-time, American hams are forbidden to communicate with certain countries. Usually the "forbidden" list is based on political considerations either by our government or theirs. The ARRL stays current on the shifting winds and can advise you on countries which should be avoided. (N1H02)

And Now, A Word From Our Sponsor

Most of the rules which regulate Amateurs are based on common sense. For example, if commercial activities were permitted, it would destroy the Amateur Service. Can you imagine some large company or distributor broadcasting advertisements on your

favorite ham band? Soon everyone would do it and there would be no room left for Amateur activities.

By the same token, you cannot use your ham radio for broadcasting. Broadcasting is defined as *one-way transmissions intended for reception by the general public*. Broadcasting of bulletins solely of interest to radio Amateurs (such as the Newsline Report) is permitted. But there is no way you can broadcast "Hi, this is Fuzzy Fred from Farmingdale with all the latest hits and Top 40 tunes." To emphasize the point, the transmission of *music on ham radio is strictly forbidden*. (N1I06)(N1I07)(T1E01) (T1E02)

Several organizations transmit information bulletins and code practice. For example, the ARRL operates a code practice and news bulletin station for Amateurs. The call letters are W1AW, with transmitters located in Newington, CT. W1AW is an extensive operation which requires several employees of the League to manage. Some time ago they realized that, in the strict sense, these employees were receiving compensation for sending messages on the Amateur bands. An Amateur station can never be hired to transmit messages. Thus, the rules were modified slightly to state that the control operator can be paid if they work for a station that sends code practice or news bulletins to Amateurs. (N1I05)

Note that beacon operation, radio control, emergency communication and information bulletins for Amateurs, and Morse code practice are **not** considered to be broadcasting.

There's Show Business Like No Business

Even if your dad wants to use your radio to order a pizza, he can't. It's illegal and you have to tell him so. *Business communications via Amateur Radio are never permitted* unless it involves the immediate safety of life of individuals or property is threatened. Even if ham radio activities are involved (for example business planning for your ham club or requesting a club membership application), you can't "talk business" on Amateur Radio. (N1H03)(N1H04)(N1H05)

You should exercise *good judgement* about messages you handle, with respect to the law on business communication. "Your cousin just had a baby", or some such, is certainly permitted. "Henry, your XYL is shipping your HF rig Monday. You should have it by the end of the week" probably would not raise any eyebrows. However, "Hey Sam, the 'widgets' you ordered aren't available with .35 hole spacing. Will you accept 0.5?" is certainly "over the line." I'm sure you get the idea.

When handling messages you cannot accept any compensation for your services. If you did, it would be a *business transaction*, which is clearly and absolutely forbidden. By the way, compensation does not mean simply money. You cannot accept goods, services, favors or any sort of reward for handling messages. (T1E03)

There is one situation where you could use ham radio to aid a business. This might occur during an emergency. Let's say you are providing communications during a flood. You might say "If we don't get some sandbags down here to the Ajax building, it's going to wash away." If the sandbags were delivered and the building was saved, you certainly used Amateur Radio to aid the businesses in the building. But you also saved the building from certain destruction and maybe even saved a life (someone might try to get their belongings out of the building). While this is a hypothetical situation, I'm sure you understand the intent of the law.

He Can't Say That, Can He?

It is inconceivable that an Amateur would send false signals or that they need to be cautioned about doing so. However, you will probably be asked a question to make sure you understand that *false and deceptive signals are absolutely forbidden*. For example, sending MAYDAY or SOS when there is no emergency is a "hanging offense" (not quite, but maybe it should be!). The same is true for "jokers" who create harmful interference on public safety (police and fire) frequencies which interrupts communication. (N1J02)(N1J04)(N1J05)

With the possible exception of "pig-Latin", you are not permitted to transmit messages in code or ciphers. The FCC **must** be able to monitor what you are saying. Since *English* is understood by all FCC monitoring stations, it *must be used for station identification*. The *CW* emission may be used anywhere in a ham band and thus it *can always be used* to identify an Amateur station. (T1B07)

Even if English is used, a foreign monitoring station might have trouble understanding your call sign, particuarly if there is interference. The FCC rules suggest that you use the International standard phonetic alphabet which is shown in the chart, *Figure 2-1* in *Chapter Two*. (T1D03)(T1D04)

Abbreviations or substitutions (other than a standard phonetic alphabet) which obscure the meaning of a message are just another form of coding. They are not permitted either. (N1I08)

Many repeaters using synthesized or digitized voice to identify their transmissions every 10 minutes. If Morse code is used for repeater identification, the transmission rate should not be faster than 20 WPM. (T1D02)

Obscene Language—It used to be that Amateurs strictly avoided discussing sex, politics or religion. But in this liberated age, these taboos have fallen by the wayside. Sadly, too, has common decency in a few cases. There will always be those "losers" who hide behind the anonymity of a microphone. They use foul language and are magically transformed, for the first time in their drab little lives, into someone that people notice.

The rules clearly and specifically state that obscene, indecent or profane words not be transmitted by an Amateur station. (T1E04)(T1E05)(T1E06)

At one time it was considered best to ignore these Neanderthals. It is my personal opinion that Amateurs have an obligation to tell these people that what they are doing is harmful to the Amateur Service and that it is not appreciated.

Third Party Traffic

Until the last 20 years or so, there was a paranoia on the part of governments about Amateurs. Their concern was not about spies but about revenue. They feared that their Post, Telephone and Telegraph (PTT) entities would lose revenue if Amateurs were allowed to handle messages into and out of their countries. As a result **third party traffic** was usually forbidden. *Third party traffic is a message passed by one Amateur control operator to another Amateur control operator on behalf of an unlicensed person.* The other person is called the third party. It is strictly forbidden to accept any sort of compensation or payment for handling third party, or any other messages, for that matter. (N1I01)(N1I09)(T1E03)

Over the intervening years, most governments have "mellowed". The United States has agreements with other governments which permit certain forms of third party traffic. If in doubt, always check with the ARRL to see if third party traffic is permitted with a specific country. The FCC also issues periodic lists of nations to which Amateurs may exchange non-commercial messages. (N1I02)(N1I10)(N1I11)(T1E08)

The Commission recognizes two categories of third party traffic: (1) other licensed Amateurs (who are eligible to be the control operator of the station); and (2) non-licensed people or organizations. Obviously the FCC is going to be more concerned about the latter category.

If the third party is present in the Amateur "shack" (the room containing the Amateur station), they are allowed to talk on the microphone even though they may not be a licensed Amateur. *The control operator must be present and continuously monitor and supervise the conversation.* Normally Amateur communications need not be identified more often than every 10 minutes. However, in the case of international third party traffic, the transmissions must be identified at the end of each exchange of communi-

cations. This allows monitoring stations to quickly identify the participants in third-party communications. (N1H10)

Out Of This World

An Amateur space station is considered to be one that is *more than 50 kilometers* above the surface of the earth. The space station may be inhabited, such as the shuttle or MIR, or it may be an OSCAR, satellite like AO-13 or the digital PAKSAT. Amateurs flying aboard the shuttle, by the way, are *required to have an Amateur Extra class operator license.* (N1I04)

Interference

Amateurs can interfere with other stations unintentionally. Sometimes interference cannot be avoided, like trying to move around in a crowded room. You'll always bump into people you are unaware of. This is unintentional and, on the Amateur bands, just part of the game. However, it is clearly unlawful to **maliciously or intentionally interfere** with another station. Interference that intentionally disturbs other communications is called **harmful interference**. This is never permitted. (N1J01) (N1J03)

If you respond to someone's call, without identifying yourself it is in violation of the FCC rules. The law states that *you must always identify your transmissions with your station call sign.* Never transmit an unmodulated and unidentified signal (except to control model craft) because it is illegal and breaks the rules twice! (N1J06) ((N1J07)(N1J09)

There is concern on the part of the FCC that you understand the rules regarding interference between primary and secondary users of a frequency. For example, on the 902 MHz band, Amateurs are the secondary users. If the primary user interferes with you, you must assume that you are also interfering with them. As the secondary user, you are required to change frequency to eliminate the possibility of interference. (T1B04)(T1B05)

If two Amateur stations are the primary users of a band, they have equal rights to a given frequency. In these instances, however, one station or the other is expected to change frequency to avoid interference. If neither station changes frequency, it could be construed as intentional interference—which is illegal. (T1B06)

This Is An Emergency!

Amateur Radio really "shines" when there is a disaster which disrupts normal communication systems in a particular area. When this happens, the FCC may declare a *temporary state of communications emergency.* This declaration is usually initiated by the FCC Engineer-in-Charge of the affected area. This official representative of the FCC will detail any *special conditions and special rules* to be observed by Amateur stations during the emergency. Generally speaking, the FCC will restrict transmissions to those necessary to meet *essential communication* needs and to facilitate relief actions. (T1E10)(T1E11)

Normally you are not allowed to communicate with stations other than those in the Amateur Service, but this is not always the case. If you or someone elses life or property is in jeopardy in an emergency, you can communicate on any frequency **by any means necessary**. In a real emergency you can transmit the international safety terms "SOS" or "MAYDAY," if necessary. (N1J10)(N1J11)

You can communicate with non-Amateur stations when authorized by the FCC. Exceptions are also made when safety is involved. For example, in an emergency the FCC would permit you to establish contact with the United States Coast Guard on frequencies outside a ham band. The FCC would also permit non-Amateur Coast Guard personnel to operate inside a band allocated to Amateur operation. This is perfectly legal. In an emergency situation, where safety of human life is involved, you would be allowed to communicate by any means or frequencies at your disposal. (N1J08)

Use your own good judgement if your safety is involved. Let's say you are piloting a pleasure boat off the coast of California. In an emergency situation, where safety of life and or the craft is involved, you could use your ham rig to contact a commercial shore station on a frequency outside a ham band.

Many mariners are getting ham tickets and installing Amateur gear on their boats. Because of their wide dispersion and activity, one is far more likely to contact a ham than a specific shore station regardless of time, distance or radio conditions.

Power Output

The FCC is concerned that you understand the in's and out's of power (no pun intended!). Let's talk about power output. As an Amateur, you are permitted to transmit a large amount of power. For example, a Technician is permitted 1,500 watts PEP output on the two-meter band (144-148 MHz). (T1B10)

Even so, there is another important rule which takes precedence over any maximum permitted power output. Part 97.313(a) states that you should *never* use more power than is necessary to carry out the desired communication. If you would like to experiment with different power output levels, you will be amazed at how little difference power makes. When the signals are strong, you can reduce power by a factor of 10 or more and still maintain perfect communications. (N1F01)

At what point does power become power output? So there is no confusion about power output measurement, the FCC specifies the power delivered by your transmitter or power amplifier to the terminals that connect to the antenna system. (T1B01)

In various places throughout this book, you will see the term "peak envelope power" (PEP) used. This refers to the measurement of power when the information or modulation of a transmitter varies the amount of power rather than the frequency. If you vary the amplitude or strength of the transmitter signal with information (data, speech, etc.), power output must be defined differently than for a steady signal. The definition of peak envelope power is *the average power supplied during one RF cycle at the crest of the modulation envelope.* (T1B02)

Beacon Stations

At various times, the high frequency Amateur bands are capable of supporting communication over great distances (see *Chapter 3-Propagation*). While there are certain patterns, it is not possible to predict with absolute certainty when a band will be "open." A popular aid to observation of propagation and reception and other related experimental activities is called a **beacon station**. The concept is simplicity itself. Every so often, the beacon transmits it's call letters and location. If you can hear the beacon at your location, you know the band is open and a "CQ" call is likely to result in a response from someone in that area. (T1D01)

The maximum permissible power output of a beacon station is *100 watts PEP*. You must hold a Technician or higher class license to operate a beacon. *Novices are not allowed* to do so. (T1B03)(T1D05)

How Wide Is My Signal?

Not only can an Amateur transmitted signal (emission) vary up and down in amplitude, but it will also vary from side to side in width. Frequency modulation is a good example of the latter. The louder you talk (without limiting), the greater the frequency excursions of the transmitter emission. If your signal is too wide, it can interfere with Amateurs operating on adjacent channels. That's why all FM transmitters incorporate *modulation deviation limiters* to prevent this from happening.

The data rate of a digital transmission has a direct bearing on the bandwidth of the transmitted emission. As the data rate increases, more modulation products are produced on each side of the carrier. These products are called *sidebands*, The sidebands result in more "real estate" being occupied by the signal. Digital modes, such as radio teletype (RTTY) and multiplexed emissions, can really "spread out" as the data rate increases.

RTTY and most digital radio transmissions use two adjacent frequencies. One represents a digital zero and the other a digital one. This is called **frequency shift keying**. On the HF Amateur bands (below 30 MHz), the FCC specifies *the maximum spacing* between the one-zero pair at 1,000 Hz or 1 kHz maximum. The maximum spacing or frequency shift is not specified above 30 MHz. (T1C02)(T1C03)

Above 30 MHz, the Commission rules specify *how wide* a digital signal can be. This includes the one-zero signal pair and the accompanying modulation products they produce. On the six and two-meter band, *the bandwidth cannot exceed 20 kHz*. On the 222 and 420 band, *the frequencies occupied can increase to 100 kHz*. (T1C10)(T1C11)

The FCC also specifies the *maximum symbol rate* permitted on various Amateur bands. For example, on 10 meters the maximum symbol rate is 1,200 bauds but it increases to 19.6 kilobauds on six and two meters. On 222 MHz, and higher in frequency, data can zip along at a symbol rate of 56 kilobauds. (T1C04)(T1C05)(T1C06)(T1C07)(T1C08)(T1C09)

Repeaters 'R Us

In almost every case, Amateur repeaters (see *Introduction* chapter) are coordinated by an area committee or ham group. If interference occurs between a coordinated and uncoordinated repeater, it is up to the licensee of the uncoordinated repeater to solve the problem. If two coordinated repeaters or uncoordinated repeaters interfere, the licensees of the repeaters are equally responsible for resolving the interference. (T1D06)(T1D07)(T1D08)

Auxiliary, repeater and space stations are all allowed to repeat Amateur transmissions, but beacon stations are specifically excluded from doing so. We Amateurs are also permitted to retransmit United States Government communications of the space shuttle with the permission of NASA. (T1E07)

Telecommand Control

Since the area of controlling remote objects has exploded, we can no longer think of just model aircraft when the subject of electronic control is discussed. Don't let the term *telecommand* confuse you, however. Telecommand used to be called *radio control* in the "good ole days."

Technicians interested in the radio control (oops- telecommand) of models, will want to investigate the six-meter band. There is a lot of unused "space" for their control systems. The interference level on six meters is considerably lower than the popular 72 MHz frequencies. The 72 MHz channels used to radio control models are crowded with commercial users and subject to interference.

Model hobbyists are increasingly attracted to the six-meter band because of the large number of clear frequencies. Because it is so easy to earn the Technician license, many hobbyists are getting their "ticket" just so they can fly their planes without fear of mishaps due to interference.

You can use a maximum of *one watt output* to control models on the Amateur bands. You need not identify your transmissions. The only requirement is that you *attach a label indicating your call letters plus your name and address, to the transmitter.* The object being controlled by radio does not need any identification since it only receives signals and does not transmit. As always, you should have a copy of your Amateur license in your possession.(T1D09)(T1D10)(T1D11)

Now that you have all this information stored in the random access memory between your ears, let's take a test. The following questions are from the Novice and Technician pool section which pertains to rules and regulations. The correct answers will be found near the end of the book. Don't be tempted to "sneak a peak." Also, write your answers on a separate sheet of paper, not on the pages of the book. You don't want to give your answers (right or wrong) to someone else who might like to study for the test.

Novice Subelement 1 (10 questions)

N1A01—What document contains the rules and regulations for the Amateur Service in the US? (A) Part 97 of Title 47 CFR (Code of Federal Regulations); (B) The Communications Act of 1934 (as amended); (C) The Radio Amateur's Handbook; (D) The minutes of the International Telecommunication Union meetings.

N1A02—Who makes and enforces the rules and regulations of the Amateur Service in the US? (A) The Congress of the United States; (B) The Federal Communications Commission (FCC); (C) The Volunteer Examiner Coordinators (VECs); (D) The Federal Bureau of Investigation (FBI).

N1A03—Which three topics are part of the rules and regulations of the Amateur Service? (A) Station operation standards, technical standards, emergency communications; (B) Notice of Violation, common operating procedures, antenna lengths; (C) Frequency band plans, repeater locations, Ohm's law; (D) Station construction standards, FCC approved radios, FCC approved antennas.

N1A04—Which of these topics is NOT part of the rules and regulations of the Amateur Service? (A) Qualifying examination systems; (B) Technical standards; (C) Providing emergency communications; (D) Station construction standards.

N1A05—What are three reasons that the Amateur Service exists? (A) To recognize the value of emergency communications, advance the radio art, and improve communication and technical skills; (B) To learn about business communications, increase testing by trained technicians, and improve Amateur communications; (C) To preserve old radio techniques, maintain a pool of people familiar with early tube-type equipment, and improve tube radios; (D) To improve patriotism, preserve nationalism, and promote world peace.

N1A06—What are two of the five purposes for the Amateur Service? (A) To protect historical radio data, and help the public understand radio history; (B) To help foreign countries improve communication and technical skills, and encourage visits from foreign hams; (C) To modernize radio schematic drawings, and increase the pool of electrical drafting people ; (D) To increase the number of trained radio operators and electronics experts, and improve international goodwill.

N1A07—What is the definition of an Amateur operator? (A) A person who has not received any training in radio operations; (B) A person who has a written authorization to be the control operator of an Amateur station; (C) A person who has very little practice operating a radio station; (D) A person who is in training to become the control operator of a radio station.

N1A08—What is the definition of the Amateur Service? (A) A private radio service used for profit and public benefit; (B) A public radio service for US citizens which requires no exam; (C) A personal radio service used for self-training, communication, and technical studies; (D) A private radio service used for self-training of radio announcers and technicians.

N1A09—What is the definition of an Amateur station? (A) A station in a public radio service used for radiocommunications; (B) A station using radiocommunications for a commercial purpose; (C) A station using equipment for training new radiocommunications operators; (D) A station in an Amateur Radio Service used for radiocommunications.

N1A10—What is the definition of a control operator of an Amateur station? (A) Anyone who operates the controls of the station; (B) Anyone who is responsible for the station's equipment; (C) Any licensed Amateur operator who is responsible for the station's transmissions; (D) The Amateur operator with the highest class of license who is near the controls of the station.

N1A11—What is a Volunteer Examiner (VE)? (A) An Amateur who volunteers to check Amateur teaching manuals; (B) An Amateur who volunteers to teach Amateur classes; (C) An Amateur who volunteers to test others for Amateur licenses; (D) An Amateur who volunteers to examine Amateur station equipment

N1B01—Which one of these must you have an Amateur license to do? (A) Transmit on public-service frequencies; (B) Retransmit shortwave broadcasts; (C) Repair broadcast station equipment; (D) Transmit on Amateur Service frequencies.

N1B02—What does an Amateur license allow you to control? (A) A shortwave-broadcast station's transmissions; (B) An Amateur station's transmissions; (C) Non-commercial FM broadcast transmissions; (D) Any type of transmitter, as long as it is used for non-commercial transmissions.

N1B03—What allows someone to operate an Amateur station in the US? (A) An FCC operator's training permit for a licensed radio station; (B) An FCC Form 610 together with a license examination fee; (C) An FCC Amateur operator/primary station license; (D) An FCC Certificate of Successful Completion of Amateur Training.

N1B04—Where does a US Amateur license allow you to operate? (A) Anywhere in the world; (B) Wherever the Amateur Service is regulated by the FCC; (C) Within 50 km of your primary station location; (D) Only at your primary station location.

N1B05—If you have a Novice license, how many transmitters may you control in your station at the same time? (A) Only one at a time; (B) Only one at a time, except for emergency communications; (C) Any number; (D) Any number, as long as they are transmitting on different bands.

N1B06—What document must you keep at your Amateur station? (A) A copy of your written authorization for an Amateur station; (B) A copy of the Rules and Regulations of the Amateur Service (Part 97); (C) A copy of the Amateur Radio Handbook for instant reference; (D) A chart of the frequencies allowed for your class of license.

N1B07—Which one of the following does not allow a person to control a US Amateur station? (A) An operator/primary station license from the FCC; (B) A reciprocal permit for alien Amateur licensee from the FCC; (C) An Amateur Service license from any government which is a member of the European Community (EC); (D) An Amateur Service license from the Government of Canada, if it is held by a Canadian citizen.

N1B08—What are the five US Amateur operator license classes? (A) Novice, Communicator, General, Advanced, Amateur Extra; (B) Novice, Technician, General, Advanced, Expert; (C) Novice, Communicator, General, Amateur, Extra; (D) Novice, Technician, General, Advanced, Amateur Extra.

N1B09—What does the FCC consider to be the first two classes of US Amateur operator licenses (one of which most new Amateurs initially hold)? (A) Novice and Technician; (B) CB and Communicator; (C) Novice and General; (D) CB and Novice.

N1B10—What must you have with you when you are the control operator of an Amateur station? (A) A copy of the Rules and Regulations of the Amateur Service (Part 97); (B) The original or a photocopy of your Amateur license; (C) A list of countries which allow third-party communications from the US; (D) A chart of the frequencies allowed for your class of license.

N1B11—Which US Amateur license has no Morse code requirements? (A) Amateur Extra; (B) Advanced; (C) General; (D) Technician.

N1C01—What are the frequency limits of the 80-meter Novice band? (A) 3500 - 4000 kHz; (B) 3675 - 3725 kHz; (C) 7100 - 7150 kHz; (D) 7000 - 7300 kHz.

N1C02—What are the frequency limits of the 40-meter Novice band (ITU Region 2)? (A) 3500 - 4000 kHz; (B) 3700 - 3750 kHz; (C) 7100 - 7150 kHz; (D) 7000 - 7300 kHz.

N1C03—What are the frequency limits of the 15-meter Novice band? (A) 21.100 - 21.200 MHz; (B) 21.000 - 21.450 MHz; (C) 28.000 - 29.700 MHz; (D) 28.100 - 28.200 MHz.

N1C04—What are the frequency limits of the 10-meter Novice band? (A) 28.000 - 28.500 MHz; (B) 28.100 - 29.500 MHz; (C) 28.100 - 28.500 MHz; (D) 29.100 - 29.500 MHz.

N1C05—What are the frequency limits of the 1.25-meter Novice band (ITU Region 2)? (A) 225.0 - 230.5 MHz; (B) 222.1 - 223.91 MHz; (C) 224.1 - 225.1 MHz; (D) 222 - 225 MHz.

N1C06—What are the frequency limits of the 23-centimeter Novice band? (A) 1260 - 1270 MHz; (B) 1240 - 1300 MHz; (C) 1270 - 1295 MHz; (D) 1240 - 1246 MHz.

N1C07—If you are operating on 3700 kHz, in what Amateur band are you operating? (A) 80 meters; (B) 40 meters; (C) 15 meters; (D) 10 meters.

N1C08—If you are operating on 7125 kHz, in what Amateur band are you operating? (A) 80 meters; (B) 40 meters; (C) 15 meters; (D) 10 meters.

N1C09—If you are operating on 21.150 MHz, in what Amateur band are you operating? (A) 80 meters; (B) 40 meters; (C) 15 meters; (D) 10 meters.

N1C10—If you are operating on 28.150 MHz, in what Amateur band are you operating? (A) 80 meters; (B) 40 meters; (C) 15 meters; (D) 10 meters.

N1C11—If you are operating on 223 MHz, in what Amateur band are you operating? (A) 15 meters; (B) 10 meters; (C) 2 meters; (D) 1.25 meters.

N1D01—Who can become an Amateur licensee in the US? (A) Anyone except a representative of a foreign government; (B) Only a citizen of the United States; (C) Anyone except an employee of the US government; (D) Anyone.

N1D02—What age must you be to hold an Amateur license? (A) 14 years or older; (B) 18 years or older; (C) 70 years or younger; (D) There are no age limits.

N1D03—What minimum examinations must you pass for a Novice Amateur license? (A) A written exam, Element 1(A); and a 5 WPM code exam, Element 2(A); (B) A 5 WPM code exam, Element 1(A); and a written exam, Element 3(A); (C) A 5 WPM code exam, Element 1(A); and a written exam, Element 2; (D) A written exam, Element 2; and a 5 WPM code exam, Element 4.

N1D04—Why must an Amateur operator have a current US Postal mailing address? (A) So the FCC has a record of the location of each Amateur station; (B) To follow the FCC rules and so the licensee can receive mail from the FCC; (C) So the FCC can send license-renewal notices; (D) So the FCC can publish a call-sign directory.

N1D05—What must you do to replace your license if it is lost, mutilated or destroyed? (A) Nothing; no replacement is needed; (B) Send a change of address to the FCC using a current FCC Form 610; (C) Retake all examination elements for your license; (D) Request a new one from the FCC, explaining what happened to the original.

N1D06—What must you do to notify the FCC if your mailing address changes? (A) Fill out an FCC Form 610 using your new address, attach a copy of your license, and mail it to your local FCC Field Office; (B) Fill out an FCC Form 610 using your new address, attach a copy of your license, and mail it to the FCC office in Gettysburg, PA; (C) Call your local FCC Field Office and give them your new address over the phone; (D) Call the FCC office in Gettysburg, PA, and give them your new address over the phone.

N1D07—Which of the following call signs is a valid US Amateur call? (A) UA4HAK; (B) KBL7766; (C) KA9OLS; (D) BY7HY.

N1D08—What letters must be used for the first letter in US Amateur call signs? (A) K, N, U and W; (B) A, K, N and W; (C) A, B, C and D; (D) A, N, V and W.

N1D09—What numbers are normally used in US Amateur call signs? (A) Any two-digit number, 10 through 99; (B) Any two-digit number, 22 through 45; (C) A single digit, 1 though 9; (D) A single digit, 0 through 9.

N1D10—For how many years is an Amateur license normally issued? (A) 2; (B) 5; (C) 10; (D) 15.

N1D11—How soon before your license expires should you send the FCC a completed 610 for a renewal? (A) 60 to 90 days; (B) within 21 days of the expiration date; (C) 6 to 9 months; (D) 6 months to a year.

N1E01—What emission types are Novice control operators allowed to use in the 80-meter band? (A) CW only; (B) Data only; (C) RTTY only; (D) Phone only.

N1E02—What emission types are Novice control operators allowed to use in the 40-meter band? (A) CW only; (B) Data only; (C) RTTY only; (D) Phone only.

N1E03—What emission types are Novice control operators allowed to use in the 15-meter band? (A) CW only; (B) Data only; (C) RTTY only; (D) Phone only.

N1E04—What emission types are Novice control operators allowed to use from 3675 to 3725 kHz? (A) Phone only; (B) Image only; (C) Data only; (D) CW only.

N1E05—What emission types are Novice control operators allowed to use from 7100 to 7150 kHz in ITU Region 2? (A) CW and data; (B) Phone; (C) Data only; (D) CW only.

N1E06—What emission types are Novice control operators allowed to use on frequencies from 21.1 to 21.2 MHz? (A) CW and data; (B) CW and phone; (C) Data only; (D) CW only.

N1E07—What emission types are Novice control operators allowed to use on frequencies from 28.1 to 28.3 MHz? (A) All authorized Amateur emission privileges; (B) Data or phone; (C) CW, RTTY and data; (D) CW and phone.

N1E08—What emission types are Novice control operators allowed to use on frequencies from 28.3 to 28.5 MHz? (A) All authorized Amateur emission privileges; (B) CW and data; (C) CW and single-sideband phone; (D) Data and phone.

N1E09—What emission types are Novice control operators allowed to use on the Amateur 1.25-meter band in ITU Region 2? (A) CW and phone; (B) CW and data; (C) Data and phone; (D) All Amateur emission privileges authorized for use on the band.

N1E10—What emission types are Novice control operators allowed to use on the Amateur 23-centimeter band? (A) Data and phone; (B) CW and data; (C) CW and phone; (D) All Amateur emission privileges authorized for use on the band.

N1E11—On what HF frequencies may Novice control operators use single-sideband (SSB) phone? (A) 3700 - 3750 kHz; (B) 7100 - 7150 kHz; (C) 21100 - 21200 kHz; (D) 28300 - 28500 kHz.

N1E12—On what frequencies in ITU Region 2 may Novice control operators use FM phone? (A) 28.3 - 28.5 MHz; (B) 144.0 - 148.0 MHz; (C) 222.1 - 223.91 MHz; (D) 1240 - 1270 MHz.

N1E13—On what frequencies in the 10-meter band may Novice control operators use RTTY? (A) 28.0 - 28.3 MHz; (B) 28.1 - 28.3 MHz; (C) 28.0 - 29.3 MHz; (D) 29.1 - 29.3 MHz.

N1E14—On what frequencies in the 10-meter band may Novice control operators use data emissions? (A) 28.0 - 28.3 MHz; (B) 28.1 - 28.3 MHz; (C) 28.0 - 29.3 MHz; (D) 29.1 - 29.3 MHz.

N1F01—What amount of transmitter power must Amateur stations use at all times? (A) 25 watts PEP output; (B) 250 watts PEP output; (C) 1500 watts PEP output; (D) The minimum legal power necessary to communicate.

N1F02—What is the most transmitter power an Amateur station may use on 3700 kHz? (A) 5 watts PEP output; (B) 25 watts PEP output; (C) 200 watts PEP output; (D) 1500 watts PEP output.

N1F03—What is the most transmitter power an Amateur station may use on 7125 kHz? (A) 5 watts PEP output; (B) 25 watts PEP output; (C) 200 watts PEP output; (D) 1500 watts PEP output.

N1F04—What is the most transmitter power an Amateur station may use on 21.125 MHz? (A) 5 watts PEP output; (B) 25 watts PEP output; (C) 200 watts PEP output; (D) 1500 watts PEP output.

N1F05—What is the most transmitter power a Novice station may use on 28.125 MHz? (A) 5 watts PEP output; (B) 25 watts PEP output; (C) 200 watts PEP output; (D) 1500 watts PEP output.

N1F06—What is the most transmitter power a Novice station may use on the 10-meter band? (A) 5 watts PEP output; (B) 25 watts PEP output; (C) 200 watts PEP output; (D) 1500 watts PEP output.

N1F07—What is the most transmitter power a Novice station may use on the 1.25-meter band? (A) 5 watts PEP output; (B) 25 watts PEP output; (C) 200 watts PEP output; (D) 1500 watts PEP output.

N1F08—What is the most transmitter power a Novice station may use on the 23-centimeter band? (A) 5 watts PEP output; (B) 25 watts PEP output; (C) 200 watts PEP output; (D) 1500 watts PEP output.

N1F09—On which bands may a Novice station use up to 200 watts PEP output power? (A) 80, 40, 15, and 10 meters; (B) 80, 40, 20, and 10 meters; (C) 1.25 meters; (D) 23 centimeters.

N1F10—On which bands must a Novice station use no more than 25 watts PEP output power? (A) 80, 40, 15, and 10 meters; (B) 80, 40, 20, and 10 meters; (C) 1.25 meters; (D) 23 centimeters.

N1F11—On which bands must a Novice station use no more than 5 watts PEP output power? (A) 80, 40, 15, and 10 meters; (B) 80, 40, 20, and 10 meters; (C) 1.25 meters; (D) 23 centimeters.

N1G01—If you allow another Amateur to be responsible for the transmissions from your station, what is the other operator called? (A) An auxiliary operator; (B) The operations coordinator; (C) A third-party operator; (D) A control operator.

N1G02—Who is responsible for the proper operation of an Amateur station? (A) Only the control operator; (B) Only the station licensee; (C) Both the control operator and the station licensee; (D) The person who owns the station equipment.

N1G03—If you transmit from another Amateur's station, who is responsible for its proper operation? (A) Both of you; (B) The other Amateur (the station licensee); (C) You, the control operator; (D) The station licensee, unless the station records show that you were the control operator at the time.

N1G04—What is your responsibility as a station licensee? (A) You must allow another Amateur to operate your station upon request; (B) You must be present whenever the station is operated; (C) You must notify the FCC if another Amateur acts as the control operator; (D) You are responsible for the proper operation of the station in accordance with the FCC rules.

N1G05—Who may be the control operator of an Amateur station? (A) Any person over 21 years of age; (B) Any person over 21 years of age with a General class license or higher; (C) Any licensed Amateur chosen by the station licensee; (D) Any licensed Amateur with a Technician class license or higher.

N1G06—If another Amateur transmits from your station, which of these is NOT true? (A) You must first give permission for the other Amateur to use your station; (B) You must keep the call sign of the other Amateur, together with the time and date of transmissions, in your station records; (C) The FCC will think that you are the station's control operator unless your station records show that you were not; (D) Both of you are equally responsible for the proper operation of the station.

N1G07—If you let another Amateur with a higher class license than yours control your station, what operating privileges are allowed? (A) Any privileges allowed by the higher license; (B) Only the privileges allowed by your license; (C) All the emission privileges of the higher license, but only the frequency privileges of your license; (D) All the frequency privileges of the higher license, but only the emission privileges of your license.

N1G08—If you are the control operator at the station of another Amateur who has a higher class license than yours, what operating privileges are you allowed? (A) Any privileges allowed by the higher license; (B) Only the privileges allowed by your license; (C) All the emission privileges of the higher license, but only the frequency privileges of your license; (D) All the frequency privileges of the higher license, but only the emission privileges of your license.

N1G09—When must an Amateur station have a control operator? (A) Only when training another Amateur; (B) Whenever the station receiver is operated; (C) Whenever the station is transmitting; (D) A control operator is not needed.

N1G10—When a Novice station is transmitting, where must its control operator be? (A) At the station's control point; (B) Anywhere in the same building as the transmitter; (C) At the station's entrance, to control entry to the room; (D) Anywhere within 50 km of the station location.

N1G11—Why can't unlicensed persons in your family transmit using your Amateur station if they are alone with your equipment? (A) They must not use your equipment without your permission; (B) They must be licensed before they are allowed to be control operators; (C) They must first know how to use the right abbreviations and Q signals; (D) They must first know the right frequencies and emissions for transmitting.

N1H01—When may you operate your Amateur station somewhere in the US besides the location listed on your license? (A) Only during times of emergency; (B) Only after giving proper notice to the FCC; (C) During an emergency or an FCC-approved emergency practice; (D) Whenever you want to.

N1H02—With which non-Amateur stations is a US Amateur station allowed to communicate? (A) No non-Amateur stations; (B) All non-Amateur stations; (C) Only those authorized by the FCC; (D) Only those who use international Morse code.

N1H03—When are communications for business allowed in the Amateur Service? (A) Only if they are for the safety of human life or immediate protection of property; (B) There are no rules against business communications; (C) No business communications are ever allowed; (D) Business communications are allowed between the hours of 9 AM to 5 PM, weekdays.

N1H04—Which of the following CANNOT be discussed on an Amateur club net? (A) Business planning; (B) Recreation planning; (C) Code practice planning; (D) Emergency planning.

N1H05—If you wanted to join a radio club, would you be allowed to send a message to them via Amateur Radio requesting an application? (A) Yes, if the club is a not-for-profit organization; (B) No. This would facilitate the commercial affairs of the club; (C) Yes, but only during normal business hours, between 9 AM and 5 PM, weekdays; (D) Yes, since there are no rules against business communications in the Amateur Service.

N1H06—How often must an Amateur station be identified? (A) At the beginning of a contact and at least every ten minutes after that; (B) At least once during each transmission; (C) At least every ten minutes during and at the end of a contact; (D) At the beginning and end of each transmission.

N1H07—What do you transmit to identify your Amateur station? (A) Your "handle"; (B) Your call sign; (C) Your first name and your location; (D) Your full name.

N1H08—What identification, if any, is required when two Amateur stations begin communications? (A) No identification is required; (B) One of the stations must give both stations' call signs; (C) Each station must transmit its own call sign; (D) Both stations must transmit both call signs .

N1H09—What identification, if any, is required when two Amateur stations end communications? (A) No identification is required; (B) One of the stations must transmit both stations' call signs; (C) Each station must transmit its own call sign; (D) Both stations must transmit both call signs .

N1H10—Besides normal identification, what else must a US station do when sending third-party communications internationally? (A) The US station must transmit its own call sign at the beginning of each communication, and at least every ten minutes after that; (B) The US station must transmit both call signs at the end of each communication; (C) The US station must transmit its own call sign at the beginning of each communication, and at least every five minutes after that; (D) Each station must transmit its own call sign at the end of each communication, and at least every five minutes after that.

N1H11—What is the longest period of time an Amateur station can operate without transmitting its call sign? (A) 5 minutes; (B) 10 minutes; (C) 15 minutes; (D) 20 minutes.

N1I01—What is the definition of third-party communications? (A) A message sent between two Amateur stations for someone else; (B) Public service communications for a political party; (C) Any messages sent by Amateur stations; (D) A three-minute transmission to another Amateur.

N1I02—When are you allowed to communicate with an Amateur in a foreign country? (A) Only when the foreign Amateur uses English; (B) Only when you have permission from the FCC; (C) Only when a third-party agreement exists between the US and the foreign country; (D) At any time, unless it is not allowed by either government.

N1A03—What is an Amateur space station? (A) An Amateur station operated on an unused frequency; (B) An Amateur station awaiting its new call letters from the

FCC; (C) An Amateur station located more than 50 kilometers above the Earth's surface; (D) An Amateur station that communicates with Space Shuttles.

N1C04—Who may be the licensee of an Amateur space station? (A) An Amateur holding an Amateur Extra class operator license; (B) Any licensed Amateur operator; (C) Anyone designated by the commander of the spacecraft; (D) No one unless specifically authorized by the government.

N1I05—When may someone be paid to transmit messages from an Amateur station? (A) Only if he or she works for a public service agency such as the Red Cross; (B) Under no circumstances; (C) Only if he or she reports all such payments to the IRS; (D) Only if he or she works for a club station and special requirements are met.

N1I06—When is an Amateur allowed to broadcast information to the general public? (A) Never; (B) Only when the operator is being paid; (C) Only when broadcasts last less than 1 hour; (D) Only when broadcasts last longer than 15 minutes.

N1I07—When is an Amateur station permitted to transmit music? (A) Never; (B) Only if the music played produces no spurious emissions; (C) Only if it is used to jam an illegal transmission; (D) Only if it is above 1280 MHz.

N1I08—When is the use of codes or ciphers allowed to hide the meaning of an Amateur message? (A) Only during contests; (B) Only during nationally declared emergencies; (C) Never, except when special requirements are met; (D) Only on frequencies above 1280 MHz.

N1I09—What is a "third-party" in Amateur communications? (A) An Amateur station that breaks in to talk; (B) A person who is sent a message by Amateur communications other than a control operator who handles the message; (C) A shortwave listener who monitors Amateur communications; (D) An unlicensed control operator.

N1I10—If you are allowing a non-Amateur friend to use your station to talk to someone in the US, and a foreign station breaks in to talk to your friend, what should you do? (A) Have your friend wait until you find out if the US has a third-party agreement with the foreign station's government; (B) Stop all discussions and quickly sign off; (C) Since you can talk to any foreign Amateurs, your friend may keep talking as long as you are the control operator; (D) Report the incident to the foreign Amateur's government.

N1I11—When are you allowed to transmit a message to a station in a foreign country for a third party? (A) Anytime; (B) Never; (C) Anytime, unless there is a third-party agreement between the US and the foreign government; (D) If there is a third-party agreement with the US government, or if the third party could be the control operator

N1J01—What is a transmission called that disturbs other communications? (A) Interrupted CW; (B) Harmful interference; (C) Transponder signals; (D) Unidentified transmissions.

N1J02—Why is transmitting on a police frequency as a "joke" called harmful interference that deserves a large penalty? (A) It annoys everyone who listens; (B) It blocks police calls which might be an emergency and interrupts police communications; (C) It is in bad taste to communicate with non-Amateurs, even as a joke; (D) It is poor Amateur practice to transmit outside the Amateur bands.

N1J03—When may you deliberately interfere with another station's communications? (A) Only if the station is operating illegally; (B) Only if the station begins transmitting on a frequency you are using; (C) Never; (D) You may expect, and cause, deliberate interference because it can't be helped during crowded band conditions.

N1J04—When may false or deceptive Amateur signals or communications be transmitted? (A) Never; (B) When operating a beacon transmitter in a "fox hunt" exercise; (C) When playing a harmless "practical joke"; (D) When you need to hide the meaning of a message for secrecy.

N1J05—If an Amateur pretends there is an emergency and transmits the word "MAYDAY," what is this called? (A) A traditional greeting in May; (B) An emergency test transmission; (C) False or deceptive signals; (D) Nothing special; "MAYDAY" has no meaning in an emergency.

N1J06—When may an Amateur transmit unidentified communications? (A) Only for brief tests not meant as messages; (B) Only if it does not interfere with others; (C) Never, except to contol a model craft; (D) Only for two-way or third-party communications.

N1J07—What is an Amateur communication called that does not have the required station identification? (A) Unidentified communications or signals; (B) Reluctance modulation; (C) Test emission; (D) Tactical communication.

N1J08—If you hear a voice distress signal on a frequency outside of your license privileges, what are you allowed to do to help the station in distress? (A) You are NOT allowed to help because the frequency of the signal is outside your privileges; (B) You are allowed to help only if you keep your signals within the nearest frequency band of your privileges; (C) You are allowed to help on a frequency outside your privileges only if you use international Morse code; (D) You are allowed to help on a frequency outside your privileges in any way possible.

N1J09—If you answer someone on the air without giving your call sign, what type of communication have you just conducted? (A) Test transmission; (B) Tactical signal; (C) Packet communication; (D) Unidentified communication.

N1J10—When may you use your Amateur station to transmit an "SOS" or "MAY-DAY"? (A) Never; (B) Only at specific times (at 15 and 30 minutes after the hour); (C) In a life or property threatening emergency; (D) When the National Weather Service has announced a severe weather watch.

N1J11—When may you send a distress signal on any frequency? (A) Never; (B) In a life or property threatening emergency; (C) Only at specific times (at 15 and 30 minutes after the hour); (D) When the National Weather Service has announced a severe weather watch

Technician Subelement 1 (5 questions)

T1A01—What is the control point of an Amateur station? (A) The on/off switch of the transmitter; (B) The input/output port of a packet controller; (C) The variable frequency oscillator of a transmitter; (D) The location at which the control operator function is performed.

T1A02—What is the term for the location at which the control operator function is performed? (A) The operating desk; (B) The control point; (C) The station location; (D) The manual control location.

T1A03—What must you do to renew or change your operator/primary station license? (A) Properly fill out FCC Form 610 and send it to the FCC in Gettysburg, PA; (B) Properly fill out FCC Form 610 and send it to the nearest FCC field office; (C) Properly fill out FCC form 610 and send it to the FCC in Washington, DC; (D) An Amateur license never needs changing or renewing.

T1A04—What is the "grace period" during which the FCC will renew an expired 10-year license? (A) 2 years; (B) 5 years; (C) 10 years; (D) There is no grace period.

T1A05—Which of the following frequencies may a Technician operator who has passed a Morse code test use? (A) 7.1 - 7.2 MHz; (B) 14.1 - 14.2 MHz; (C) 21.1 - 21.2 MHz; (D) 28.1 - 29.2 MHz.

T1A06—Which operator licenses authorize privileges on 52.525 MHz? (A) Extra, Advanced only; (B) Extra, Advanced, General only; (C) Extra, Advanced, General, Technician only; (D) Extra, Advanced, General, Technician, Novice.

T1A07—Which operator licenses authorize privileges on 146.52 MHz? (A) Extra, Advanced, General, Technician, Novice; (B) Extra, Advanced, General, Technician only; (C) Extra, Advanced, General only; (D) Extra, Advanced only.

T1A08—Which operator licenses authorize privileges on 223.50 MHz? (A) Extra, Advanced, General, Technician, Novice; (B) Extra, Advanced, General, Technician only; (C) Extra, Advanced, General only; (D) Extra, Advanced only.

T1A09—Which operator licenses authorize privileges on 446.0 MHz? (A) Extra, Advanced, General, Technician, Novice; (B) Extra, Advanced, General, Technician only; (C) Extra, Advanced, General only; (D) Extra, Advanced only.

T1A10—In addition to passing the Technician written examination (Elements 2 and 3A), what must you do before you are allowed to use Amateur frequencies below 30 MHz? (A) Nothing special is needed; all Technicians may use the HF bands at any time; (B) You must notify the FCC that you intend to operate on the HF bands; (C) You must attend a class to learn about HF communications; (D) You must pass a Morse code test (either Element 1A, 1B or 1C).

T1A11—If you are a Technician licensee, what must you have to prove that you are authorized to use the Novice Amateur frequencies below 30 MHz? (A) A certificate from the FCC showing that you have notified them that you will be using the HF bands; (B) A certificate from an instructor showing that you have attended a class in HF communications; (C) Written proof of having passed a Morse code test; (D) No special proof is required before using the HF bands.

T1B01—At what point in your station is transceiver power measured? (A) At the power supply terminals inside the transmitter or amplifier; (B) At the final amplifier input terminals inside the transmitter or amplifier; (C) At the antenna terminals of the transmitter or amplifier; (D) On the antenna itself, after the feed line.

T1B02—What is the term for the average power supplied to an antenna transmission line during one RF cycle at the crest of the modulation envelope? (A) Peak transmitter power; (B) Peak output power; (C) Average radio-frequency power; (D) Peak envelope power.

T1B03—What is the maximum transmitting power permitted an Amateur station in beacon operation? (A) 10 watts PEP output; (B) 100 watts PEP output; (C) 500 watts PEP output; (D) 1500 watts PEP output.

T1B04—If the FCC rules say that the Amateur Service is a secondary user of a frequency band, and another service is a primary user, what does this mean? (A) Nothing special; all users of a frequency band have equal rights to operate; (B) Amateurs are only allowed to use the frequency band during emergencies; (C) Amateurs are allowed to use the frequency band only if they do not cause harmful interference to primary users; (D) Amateurs must increase transmitter power to overcome any interference caused by primary users.

T1B05—If you are using a frequency within a band assigned to the Amateur Service on a secondary basis, and a station assigned to the primary service on that band causes interference, what action should you take? (A) Notify the FCC's regional Engineer in Charge of the interference; (B) Increase your transmitter's power to overcome the interference ; (C) Attempt to contact the station and request that it stop the interference;

(D) Change frequencies; you may be causing harmful interference to the other station, in violation of FCC rules.

T1B06—What rule applies if two Amateur stations want to use the same frequency? (A) The station operator with a lesser class of license must yield the frequency to a higher class licensee; (B) The station operator with a lower power output must yield the frequency to the station with a higher power output; (C) Both station operators have an equal right to operate on the frequency; (D) Station operators in ITU Regions 1 and 3 must yield the frequency to stations in ITU Region 2.

T1B07—What emission type may always be used for station identification, regardless of the transmitting frequency? (A) CW; (B) RTTY; (C) MCW; (D) Phone.

T1B08—On what frequencies within the 6-meter band may phone emissions be transmitted? (A) 50.0 - 54.0 MHz only; (B) 50.1 - 54.0 MHz only; (C) 51.0 - 54.0 MHz only; (D) 52.0 - 54.0 MHz only.

T1B09—On what frequencies within the 2-meter band may image emissions be transmitted? (A) 144.1 - 148.0 MHz only; (B) 146.0 - 148.0 MHz only; (C) 144.0 - 148.0 MHz only; (D) 146.0 - 147.0 MHz only.

T1B10—What is the maximum transmitting power permitted an Amateur station on 146.52 MHz? (A) 200 watts PEP output; (B) 500 watts ERP; (C) 1000 watts DC input; (D) 1500 watts PEP output.

T1B11—Which band may NOT be used by Earth stations for satellite communications? (A) 6 meters; (B) 2 meters; (C) 70 centimeters; (D) 23 centimeters.

T1C01—If you are a Novice licensee with a Certificate of Successful Completion of Examination (CSCE) for Technician privileges, how do you identify your station when transmitting on 146.34 MHz? (A) You must give your call sign, followed by any suitable word that denotes the slant mark and the identifier "KT"; (B) You may not operate on 146.34 until your new license arrives; (C) No special form of identification is needed; (D) You must give your call sign and the location of the VE examination where you obtained the CSCE.

T1C02—What is the maximum frequency shift permitted for RTTY or data transmissions below 50 MHz? (A) 0.1 kHz; (B) 0.5 kHz; (C) 1 kHz; (D) 5 kHz.

T1C03—What is the maximum frequency shift permitted for RTTY or data transmissions above 50 MHz? (A) 0.1 kHz or the sending speed, in bauds, whichever is greater; (B) 0.5 kHz or the sending speed, in bauds, whichever is greater; (C) 5 kHz or the sending speed, in bauds, whichever is greater; (D) The FCC rules do not specify a maximum frequency shift above 50 MHz.

T1C04—What is the maximum symbol rate permitted for packet transmissions on the 10-meter band? (A) 300 bauds; (B) 1200 bauds; (C) 19.6 kilobauds; (D) 56 kilobauds.

T1C05—What is the maximum symbol rate permitted for packet transmissions on the 2-meter band? (A) 300 bauds; (B) 1200 bauds; (C) 19.6 kilobauds; (D) 56 kilobauds.

T1C06—What is the maximum symbol rate permitted for RTTY or data transmissions between 28 and 50 MHz? (A) 56 kilobauds; (B) 19.6 kilobauds; (C) 1200 bauds; (D) 300 bauds.

T1C07—What is the maximum symbol rate permitted for RTTY or data transmissions between 50 and 222 MHz? (A) 56 kilobauds; (B) 19.6 kilobauds; (C) 1200 bauds; (D) 300 bauds.

T1C08—What is the maximum authorized bandwidth of RTTY, data or multiplexed emissions using an unspecified digital code within the frequency range of 50 to 222 MHz? (A) 20 kHz; (B) 50 kHz; (C) The total bandwidth shall not exceed that of a single-sideband phone emission; (D) The total bandwidth shall not exceed 10 times that of a CW emission.

T1C09—What is the maximum symbol rate permitted for RTTY or data transmissions above 222 MHz? (A) 300 bauds; (B) 1200 bauds; (C) 19.6 kilobauds; (D) 56 kilobauds.

T1C10—What is the maximum authorized bandwidth of RTTY, data or multiplexed emissions using an unspecified digital code within the frequency range of 222 to 450 MHz? (A) 50 kHz; (B) 100 kHz; (C) 150 kHz; (D) 200 kHz.

T1C11—What is the maximum authorized bandwidth of RTTY, data or multiplexed emissions using an unspecified digital code within the 70 cm Amateur band? (A) 300 kHz; (B) 200 kHz; (C) 100 kHz; (D) 50 kHz.

T1D01—What is an Amateur station called which transmits communications for the purpose of observation of propagation and reception? (A) A beacon; (B) A repeater; (C) An auxiliary station; (D) A radio control station.

T1D02—What is the fastest code speed a repeater may use for automatic identification? (A) 13 words per minute; (B) 20 words per minute; (C) 25 words per minute; (D) There is no limitation.

T1D03—If you are using a language besides English to make a contact, what language must you use when identifying your station? (A) The language being used for the contact; (B) The language being used for the contact, providing the US has a third-party communications agreement with that country; (C) English; (D) Any language of a country which is a member of the International Telecommunication Union.

T1D04—What do the FCC rules suggest you use as an aid for correct station identification when using phone? (A) A speech compressor; (B) Q signals; (C) A phonetic alphabet; (D) Unique words of your choice.

T1D05—What minimum class of Amateur license must you hold to operate a beacon station? (A) Novice; (B) Technician; (C) General; (D) Amateur Extra.

T1D06—If a repeater is causing harmful interference to another repeater and a frequency coordinator has recommended the operation of one station only, who is responsible for resolving the interference? (A) The licensee of the unrecommended repeater; (B) Both repeater licensees; (C) The licensee of the recommended repeater; (D) The frequency coordinator.

T1D07—If a repeater is causing harmful interference to another Amateur repeater and a frequency coordinator has recommended the operation of both stations, who is responsible for resolving the interference? (A) The licensee of the repeater which has been recommended for the longest period of time; (B) The licensee of the repeater which has been recommended the most recently; (C) The frequency coordinator; (D) Both repeater licensees.

T1D08—If a repeater is causing harmful interference to another repeater and a frequency coordinator has NOT recommended either station, who is primarily responsible for resolving the interference? (A) Both repeater licensees; (B) The licensee of the repeater which has been in operation for the longest period of time; (C) The licensee of the repeater which has been in operation for the shortest period of time; (D) The frequency coordinator.

T1D09—What minimum information must be on a label affixed to a transmitter used for telecommand (control) of model craft? (A) Station call sign; (B) Station call sign and the station licensee's name; (C) Station call sign and the station licensee's name and address; (D) Station call sign and the station licensee's class of license.

T1D10—What are the station identification requirements for an Amateur transmitter used for telecommand (control) of model craft? (A) Once every ten minutes; (B) Once every ten minutes, and at the beginning and end of each transmission; (C) At the beginning and end of each transmission; (D) Station identification is not required if the transmitter is labeled with the station licensee's name, address and call sign.

T1D11—What is the maximum transmitter power an Amateur station is allowed when used for telecommand (control) of model craft? (A) One milliwatt; (B) One watt; (C) Two watts; (D) Three watts.

T1E01—What is meant by the term broadcasting? (A) Transmissions intended for reception by the general public, either direct or relayed; (B) Retransmission by automatic means of programs or signals from non-Amateur stations; (C) One-way radio communications, regardless of purpose or content; (D) One-way or two-way radio communications between two or more stations.

T1E02—Which of the following one-way communications may not be transmitted in the Amateur Service? (A) Telecommands to model craft; (B) Broadcasts intended for the general public; (C) Brief transmissions to make adjustments to the station; (D) Morse code practice.

T1E03—What kind of payment is allowed for third-party messages sent by an Amateur station? (A) Any amount agreed upon in advance; (B) Donation of equipment repairs; (C) Donation of Amateur equipment; (D) No payment of any kind is allowed.

T1E04—When may you send obscene words from your Amateur station? (A) Only when they do not cause interference to other communications; (B) Never; obscene words are prohibited in Amateur transmissions; (C) Only when they are not retransmitted through a repeater; (D) Any time, but there is an unwritten rule among Amateurs that they should not be used on the air.

T1E05—When may you send indecent words from your Amateur station? (A) Only when they do not cause interference to other communications; (B) Only when they are not retransmitted through a repeater; (C) Any time, but there is an unwritten rule among Amateurs that they should not be used on the air; (D) Never; indecent words are prohibited in Amateur transmissions.

T1E06—When may you send profane words from your Amateur station? (A) Only when they do not cause interference to other communications; (B) Only when they are not retransmitted through a repeater; (C) Never; profane words are prohibited in Amateur transmissions; (D) Any time, but there is an unwritten rule among Amateurs that they should not be used on the air.

T1E07—If you wanted to use your Amateur station to retransmit communications between a space shuttle and its associated Earth stations, what agency must first give its approval? (A) The FCC in Washington, DC; (B) The office of your local FCC Engineer In Charge (EIC); (C) The National Aeronautics and Space Administration; (D) The Department of Defense.

T1E08—When are third-party messages allowed to be sent to a foreign country? (A) When sent by agreement of both control operators; (B) When the third party speaks to a relative; (C) They are not allowed under any circumstances; (D) When the US has a third-party agreement with the foreign country or the third party is qualified to be a control operator.

T1E09—If you let an unlicensed third party use your Amateur station, what must you do at your station's control point? (A) You must continuously monitor and supervise the third party's participation; (B) You must monitor and supervise the communication only if contacts are made in countries which have no third-party communications agreement with the US; (C) You must monitor and supervise the communication only if contacts are made on frequencies below 30 MHz; (D) You must key the transmitter and make the station identification.

T1E10—If a disaster disrupts normal communication systems in an area where the Amateur Service is regulated by the FCC, what kinds of transmissions may stations make? (A) Those which are necessary to meet essential communication needs and facilitate relief actions; (B) Those which allow a commercial business to continue to operate in the affected area; (C) Those for which material compensation has been paid to the Amateur operator for delivery into the affected area; (D) Those which are to be used for program production or newsgathering for broadcasting purposes.

T1E11—What information is included in an FCC declaration of a temporary state of communication emergency? (A) A list of organizations authorized to use radio communications in the affected area; (B) A list of Amateur frequency bands to be used in the affected area; (C) Any special conditions and special rules to be observed during the emergency; (D) An operating schedule for authorized Amateur emergency stations

Chapter

Operating Procedures

When you are issued an Amateur license, it is done on the assumption you know how to properly control your station. A number of test questions are provided to insure this assumption is correct. Two questions of the 30 you will be asked from Element 2, and three questions from the 25 in Element 3A, are taken from the section called Operating Procedures.

What's That Noise?

A s an Amateur, you are permitted to operate a high power radio transmitter. In the last chapter, we discussed the rules regarding intentional interference with another station. Unless you observe good operating practice, your transmitter can also cause *unintentional interference*.

Just think what would happen if anyone could transmit anywhere they wanted to at any time. The feuding would make the Hatfield and McCoy battles seem like a sewing circle competition. The FCC would probably assign the frequencies to the public and give it a name like "The Citizens Band".

When selecting a frequency for your transmitter, the most important consideration is to insure that you minimize the interference with other Amateurs. It is common courtesy to say "Is this frequency in use?", before calling another specific Amateur or calling CQ. By the way, CQ is a procedural signal meaning *I want to make a contact*. (N2A01)(N2A08)

Although you are allowed to transmit with considerable power when you have an Amateur license, the rules say that you must reduce your power to the minimum necessary to maintain communication. If you contact a station that is very strong, don't forget to "turn down the wick" (reduce power output) to minimize interference to other stations. (N2A02)

One of the most annoying forms of interference is not confined to newcomers. Some "ole timers," who should know better, persist in tuning up their transmitters into an antenna. They do not listen (or ask) to see if the frequency is clear. Their unmodulated signal can cause annoying interfering whistles or entirely "blot out" weak signals. Transmitter tune up *should always be done* using a device called a **dummy load**. This device is sometimes called a dummy antenna. (See *Chapter 4 - Test Equipment*, page 108). The dummy load appears just like an antenna as far as the transmitter is concerned except that it does not radiate a signal. Thus there is no radio frequency energy to interfere with other operators. (N2A03)

There's nothing subtle about the interference when someone starts transmitting on top of you. There are other forms of interference which *are* subtle, however. For example, droning "CQ" on-and-on without signing your call is a form of on-the-air pollution. Rather than making filibuster CQ's, you should make crisp, short transmissions. When trying to contact another station using CW, the correct format is to send CQ three times followed by the letters **DE** (a procedural signal meaning *from, or this is*) and your call letters three times. At this point you can let up on the key long enough to see if anyone returns your call. If the band is dead or conditions are poor, you may wish to repeat the sequence a few times before listening. (N2A05)(N2A09)

The Kenwood TM-241A 144 MHz mobile rig features a TouchTone™ pad on the mike..

If you answer someone else's CQ, you should send their call twice, followed by the characters DE, followed by your call sign twice. Then standby to see if you were heard. Incidentally, your CW sending speed should be paced to the speed of the Amateur you heard sending CQ. *You should never call a station at a speed faster than you can reliably copy.* Otherwise it is necessary to take time to tell the sender to QRS (slow down). This transmission would not have been necessary if you had responded at the speed at which you wished to receive. (N2A06)(N2A07)

If there is a lot of QRM (interference) you may need to repeat the send/listen sequence a couple of times before giving up. Obviously, if the station you are calling goes back to someone else, you should stop calling.

On 10 meters, you might want to listen for beacon stations (see *Chapter 1 - Beacon Stations*) below 28.3 MHz before transmitting. Amateur beacons are low power (100 watts maximum) automatic CW stations that transmit the call letters and location of the station. It is not unusual to hear an Australian beacon when the Novice/Technician phone portion of the band (28.3-28.5 MHz) seems totally dead.

On phone, the standard format is similar to a CW call except that you do not use the term DE. Normally, you would say CQ three times, then "this is" and your call letters three times. If you respond to someone else's CQ, you should give their call once followed by "this is" and your call letters spelled out phonetically (see *Chapter 2 - The Phonetic Alphabet*). (N2A18)(N2A19)

As a practical matter, calls are often paced according to band conditions. If the band is very active, it means that many people will be tuning around looking for a contact. A short "CQ, CQ, CQ 10 meters, this is K6HX located in Del Mar, California, calling CQ 10 meters" will often suffice. If the band seems dead, you may wish to repeat the sequence several times.

Band propagation, as well as band conditions, should be considered when trying to contact a specific station. For example, if you live in Seattle and wish to contact a friend in San Diego, you wouldn't try to do it on the two meter band. Why not? Two meters, for the most part, is a VHF **line-of-sight** band. Calling a station which is out of range for the band propagation and characteristic is a subtle form of interference for other users of the band.

To work the Seattle/San Diego path (about 1,500 miles), a Novice or Tech-Plus would use the 10 or 15 meter band. Before calling your friend, you should tune around to see if there are other stations being received from that area. If not, it is likely that the call to your friend will be unsuccessful.

This CTCSS encoder-decoder (see page 74) permits tone signaling in handheld FM radios. Photo by Communications Specialists,

Procedural Signals

Amateurs use a form of shorthand to speed up their CW transmissions. These are called **procedural signals**, which are one or two letters sent together as one code character. An example, mentioned earlier, was the substitution of **DE** for the word *from* or *this is*. The most common procedural signal is **CQ**. Another is **AR** which means *over* or signifies the end of a transmission. This is different from **SK** which signifies *the* end of the contact or *good-bye*. Some of the less common procedural signals are **BT** (a double dash or equal sign), **DN** (the fraction bar, often used in call letter strings *to indicate portable operation* in another call area—i.e. W6TNS/7, Seattle). One that confuses everyone is **KN**, which means that *only the called station should transmit*. A similar pool question asks the meaning of **K** at the end of a transmission. The K (not KN) means that *any station can transmit*. Commit these abbreviations to the frontal lobe of your brain, as you will probably be asked about them during your test. (N2A08)(N2A09)(N2A10)

There are a couple of other terms you should be familar with that are not prodecural signals. One of the most common is **DX**. This means *stations from a long distance*. The term is somewhat relative. Two-meter DX might be a few hundred miles away. On 80-meter CW it could be the other coast of the United States. And on 10 meters, a DX contact might come from the other side of the world. (N2A11)

Another term you will hear is **73**, when someone ends a contact. This term means *best regards*. You occassionally hear it misused as best 73, which literally means best best regards or even best 73's, which, I supose, would translate to best best regardses—except regards is already plural! (N2A12)

By the way, the term **OM** deserves explanation. It stands for *old man* and is ham radio generic-talk for a male ham of **any age**. If your dad is a ham, he is also an old man but you may wish to exhibit a bit of discretion with the use of the term! Female hams don't seem to have an equivalent term, probably for very good reasons.

How Am I Getting Out?

Amateurs have also devised a standardized shorthand method of describing signal reception. This is called the **R-S-T** reporting system. The "R" part means the readability on a scale of one to five (barely to perfect copy). The "S" designator tells the other ham, on a scale of one to nine, their signal strength. A one would be extremely weak and unreadable, while nine would be a "rock crushing" strong signal. The ending "T" is used to indicate the tone of the CW note, again on a scale of one to nine (badly distorted to a pure musical note). A good signal from a nearby station would probably get an RST report of 599. If someone told you that you were 5-7, it would mean you were perfectly readable and moderately strong. By the token, a 3-3 would mean your signal was readable with considerable difficulty and weak in strength. (N2A13)(N2A14)(T2B09)(T2B10)

Most modern communication products include a signal strength meter. These indicators used to be calibrated with a 0-9 relative reading which corresponded to the "S" in the RST. In the 1950's, a famous ham radio manufacturing company decided to calibrate their meters in decibels (a relative strength measurement). The upper limit of the scale was 60 db (decibels). This made their products seem better than the competition which only went to S9 on the meter. Other receiver manufacturers starting printing a decibel scale on their meters too (few, if any, calibrated their receiver to the meter scale!). Most modern Amateur radios have a signal strength indicator calibrated zero to nine (which appears about mid-scale) and further graduations up to 60 on the right half of the meter. Thus, the typical signal report today might be "You are 20 db over 9 at this QTH". CW operators stick to tradition and anything over nine on the meter gets a nine in the RST report. (T2B11)

The "T" (tone) designator is dropped for phone and there is no correlation with the old RST system. One often hears the "Q" designator substituted for the "R". The "Q" stands for a general, overall indication of quality. It is correct etiquette to say "I hear you Q5-S9, OM" or simply "you are 5-9."

What's A Que-Tee-Ach?

Amateurs use another form of shorthand, called **Q-signals**. They were developed many years ago by hams to save time sending telegraphic messages. Here are a few of the more common Q-signals (some of which you may be asked on the Novice test).

QRL- Used to ask if the frequency is in use.
QRS- This Q-signal means "Send more slowly".
QRT- Means to stop sending as in "I have to QRT now for dinner".
QRZ- "Who is the station calling me?"
QSL- Acknowledgement of transmission copy such as "QSL your message number five". A QSL card is a document which confirms a two-way transmission.
QSO- A conversation on the ham radio.
QSY- To change frequency such as "QSY down 15" (kHz).
QTH- A location of the ham radio station such as "QTH- Mercer Island".

These Q-signals are in the question pool and you may be asked to identify one of them. (N2A15)(N2A16)(T2B05)(T2B06)(T2B07)(T2B08)

One interesting variation is the term **QSL**. It means *how do you copy me?* It has also be adopted for the name of the postal cards (QSL cards) that Amateurs exchange to confirm their on-the-air contacts. (N2A17)

Here are some of the other commonly used Q-signals for your information.

QRK- "What is my signal like?" You would probably respond with a Q-signal. Consider the elegant simplicity of three CW letters (QRK) and the response, "479". It may not seem important with an occasional ham contact but what if you were a telegrapher handling hundreds of messages each day?

QRM- Man-made interference such as other nearby signals, motors, ignition noise, etc.

QRN- Natural static such as lightning bursts and static crashes.

QRX- "Please stand by" or "I am standing by", depending on how it is used. For example, "Please QRX while I answer the phone".

QSB- Fading of signals due to atmospheric conditions.

QSM- "Can you repeat the last message?"

The Phonetic Alphabet

In the presence of fading, static or other forms of QRM, it is easy to mistake A6HX for K6HX. To avoid this, the International Telecommunication Union, in Geneva, Switzerland, has developed a standard **phonetic alphabet**. The words they have picked to represent the 26 letters of the alphabet are those *which are least likely to be confused* with other words on a world-wide basis.

The phonetic representations are shown in *Figure 2-1*. It is unlikely that Kilo Six Hotel X-Ray would be mistaken for A6HX. Kilo and Alpha do not sound alike but "K" and "A" sound almost the same, particularly at the other end of a noisy or weak communications circuit. (N2A20)

You must memorize the correspondence between letters and the standard phonetic words. You will be using these forever (at least until the ITU changes them) so long

A- Alpha	**J- Juliette**	**S- Sierra**
B- Bravo	**K- Kilo**	**T- Tango**
C- Charlie	**L- Lima**	**U- Uniform**
D- Delta	**M- Mike**	**V- Victor**
E- Echo	**N- November**	**W- Whiskey**
F- Foxtrot	**O- Oscar**	**X- X-Ray**
G- Golf	**P- Papa**	**Y- Yankee**
H- Hotel	**Q- Quebec**	**Z- Zulu**
I- India	**R- Romeo**	

Figure 2-1 The International Telecommunication Union Phonetic Alphabet

as you are an Amateur. The best way to commit these to memory is to spell out words phonetically on the signs you see along the highway as you are traveling. After a while they will become second nature to you. Have you got that Oscar-Kilo?

Ones And Zeros Replace Dits and Dahs

Long before the computer era, Amateurs were engaging in an early form of digital communications called **radio teletype (RTTY)**. A teletype machine is a mechanical device designed to reproduce alphanumeric characters sent from one place to another. The transport medium can be wire or radio.

The teletype machine has a selector mechanism which determines what character is printed on a paper roll or strip fed through the RTTY machine. A train of ones and zeros determines what character is selected and printed each time the motorized distributor revolves. The speed of the motor rotation determines the data or "baud" rate. Most Amateurs used 45 baud for sending and receiving communication. This amounts to about five printed characters per second.

If someone calls you on RTTY, you should answer them at the same speed or baud as the received signal. The correct format when you call CQ on RTTY is to send CQ three to six times, followed by DE, followed by your call sign sent three times. (N2B01)(N2B02)

In addition to the machines being slow, noisy and cantankerous, RTTY is prone to errors. The error correction and message addressing and routing is very rudimentary. RTTY was revolutionized (as was most everything else) with the introduction of computers. Amateurs carried the revolution one step further with the introduction of packet radio. This scheme splits any message into packets of information by a device called a **Terminal Node Controller (TNC)**. Each packet has the sender's and recipient's address or identification. In addition, packet communication includes a foolproof method of telling if the message has been corrupted by errors. If so, the sending station receives a *retransmission request*. Thus, the data you receive is error-free.

The TNC has the capability of storing a marked message (to a specific addressee) and then repeating it error-free to the recipient. When used in this mode, the TNC is called a digital repeater or **digipeater**. Because of this capability, an unlimited number of TNC's can be interconnected into a packet radio **network** for passing messages. The network can move information anywhere a TNC is located. (N2B05) (N2B06)

The PK-88 Packet Controller is one of the most popular produced by Advanced Electronics Applications (AEA).

By using an addressing scheme, many messages for different Amateurs can fly back and forth on the same frequency. You normally do not see any messages except those addressed to you. Your equipment simply monitors the traffic flow on a channel. You can display messages meant for others by entering the *monitoring mode* of your TNC. The message content will appear on your CRT screen even though the message is not addressed to you. (N2B04)

If a transmitting station sends data specifically addressed to your receiving site, you will see the words **CONNECTED** on your screen. (N2B03)

If you are interested in connecting your computer to an Amateur Radio packet network, get a copy of *How To Get Started In Packet Radio* by Dave Ingram, K4TWJ. It can be obtained from your nearest ham dealer or directly from NARA.

Repeater Etiquette For Beginners

Once again, in this chapter, the subject of repeaters comes up. The Commission wants to be sure that you have a complete understanding of repeater operation.

As mentioned in the first chapter, repeaters are used to *extend the operating range* of portable and mobile stations. You will recall that a repeater receives on frequency "A" and retransmits whatever it picks up on frequency "B." The receiving frequency is called the input and the transmitting frequency is called the output. You need to know both these frequencies so that you can set up your transceiver in repeater mode. (N2B10)(N2B11)(N2B12)(T2A05)

A common mistake of newcomers when using a repeater is to tell the station they are talking to that "I am receiving you 20 over S9" or something similar. What they are actually doing is receiving the repeater at 20 over S9. This has no relevance to the strength of the station being received by the repeater.

In FM communications, we usually speak in terms of *quieting*. Ever notice when you back off the squelch, you hear a loud hissing noise on your handheld radio? The strength of the received signal determines how much of this noise is removed. What the newcomer should have said is "I am receiving you full quieting" (meaning there is no background noise). (T2A09)(T2A10)

The ICOM IC-2 dual band transceiver operates on the 2-meter band as well as 70 cm. It is one of the most popular handhelds for beginners.

Not all repeaters are the same. Some may operate exclusively for the members of a group or club who financially support its maintenance. These are called *closed* repeaters and you must have a special permission or equipment to access them. Most repeaters are open to everyone, however. As you might suspect, these are called *open* repeaters. (T2A11)(T2A16)

You should use proper etiquette on a repeater just as you would on any other Amateur frequency. Since the reception is so crystal clear, there is no need to give call signs more than once. If you do, it brands you as a "lid" (a poor operator). When using the repeater, simply call the station you want to talk to and identify your own station. (N2B09)(T2A01)

Most repeaters use a "courtesy tone" or "beep" to indicate a station has stopped transmitting. You should wait a few seconds after the "beep" before transmitting. This allows a station to break in, if they need access to the repeater. If you do not wait for the courtesy tone, you may time-out the repeater. (T2A02)(T2A04)(T2A08)

If you are physically near the station you wish to contact, there is no need to use the wide area capability of a repeater. You can determine the location of the other station simply by asking them what is their QTH (location). You can also listen on the input frequency of the repeater to see if you can hear the station. If the station is nearby, you can switch over to a mutually agreed simplex frequency. *Simplex means that you transmit and listen on the same frequency.* Always use a simplex channel whenever a contact is possible without using the repeater. This leaves the repeater channel clear for someone else to use. (N2B07)(N2B08)(T2A18)(T2B01)(T2B02)(T2B03)

Common sense dictates that you would not use a high frequency (HF) band to chat with someone across town. Your local transmissions would also traverse great distances by skywave and might interfere with communications in another state or country. (T2A15)

Ever wonder what a repeater looks like? The unit shown is the ICOM IC-RP4520 repeater designed for the 440 MHz band.

There are other good manners which should be observed if the repeater has an autopatch function. An autopatch is a device that allows repeater users to make telephone calls from their portable handheld or mobile station. Make your calls short and to the point so that you do not tie up the repeater. (N2B13)

I cannot overstress the importance of not "hogging" the repeater. If you are talking to someone else, try to keep your transmissions short so that someone could call in an emergency. Repeaters are required by the FCC to have a **time-out device** (appropriately called a timer). It is set to switch off after three minutes (or less) of continuous transmission so that the repeater cannot be accidentally stuck in the transmitting mode. (N2B14)(T2A03)(T2A06)

There is one more aspect of repeater operation with which you must become familar. Because of the high density of repeaters in heavily populated areas, it is possible to key several repeaters when you transmit. An example might be if your station was located at a high elevation. The signals could travel far enough to key repeaters other than the one you are calling.

To avoid this, a system called **CTCSS (Continuous Tone Coded Subaudible Squelch)** or PL (a Motorola trademark for *Private Line* and a misnomer for CTCSS) is used by Amateurs. When you transmit with CTCSS, your rig also sends out a *subaudible tone*. This tone is used to key the repeater into operation. Various repeaters on the same channel will used different CTCSS tone frequencies. However, this means that you must use the correct CTCSS tone for the repeater you are calling. If you do not switch the CTCSS function of your rig on, you can call the repeater until you are "blue-in-the-face" and you will not key the repeater. (N2B15)

Repeater Interference

Whether simplex or duplex, HF or VHF, you should always use a dummy load when testing your transmitter. But there are other ways you can cause inteference and not even be aware of it! (N2A17)

Let's say you are visiting a friend in a nearby state. You both operate two meters. By telephone, you tell the friend to listen for you on 147.60 MHz simplex. As you approach your friend's city, you hear him calling you and he "talks you in", right to his driveway. Everything worked out great. Or did it?

The frequency of 147.60 happens to be the input for the local repeater. While you and your friend are chatting away, the repeater is picking you up and retransmitting your conversations on 147.00 MHz. This, of course, totally locks up the repeater preventing anyone else from using it. It's unintentional and you are unaware of the problem you have caused, but it still drives the repeater users "up the wall."

For this reason, the FCC wants you to understand about repeater input-output spacing. On the *six-meter band*, the I/O spacing is *one megaHertz (MHz)*. On *two meters* it is *600 kiloHertz (kHz)*. The output frequency that you hear may be 600 kHz higher or lower than the input or receive frequency. A repeater directory will indicate which it is with a plus or minus sign specifying your transmit frequency. The I/O spacing increases to *1.6 MHz (1600 kHz)* on the *1.25 meter band* and *5 MHz* on the *70 cm. band*. If you know these spacings and have a repeater directory, you can avoid operating on one of the repeater input frequencies. (T2A12)(T2A13)(T2A14)

If you operate simplex and interfere with a repeater, good Amateur practice dictates that you change frequency for several reasons. *The repeater is probably frequency coordinated* and has a right to be on the assigned frequency. Further, a repeater is usually crystal controlled which makes it very difficult to change the repeater frequency.

What is frequency coordination? To minimize interference between repeaters in each area, a person or group studies the situation and recommends frequency input-output pairs for repeater usage. (T2B04)

During periods when usage is low, repeaters often handle nets (shorthand for "networks"). Nets are groups of people who have a common interest. The activity may involve personally owned equipment trading, YL (young lady) meetings and third party message handling. Naturally these nets should avoid tying up the repeater during traffic rush hours. (T2A07)

Emergency Communications

One never knows when an emergency is going to occur. You could be chatting away with a friend on the local repeater or talking with a ham across the country on 10 meters. Suddenly, you hear someone say "break-break with emergency traffic." What should you do? The law requires that you *immediately standby to copy the emergency communications*. (N2A04)

You might use the above procedure to report an accident where injuries appear to be involved. In more serious situations (there's more water inside the boat than outside!), you would simply say the word *MAYDAY* several times along with your call. On **CW**, the equivalent of MAYDAY is the famous three letters *SOS*. If you need help and are in communication with a repeater, say *BREAK* twice and your call sign. You should *never use the term break on a repeater unless it is an emergency*. (T2C01)(T2C02)(T2C03)

You will recall from *Chapter 1*, the first Amateur Principle is the "recognition of emergency communications." Amateurs have banded into an important group called The Radio Amateur Civil Emergency Service (RACES). If you are interested in using your Amateur station to serve the public, you should contact your local civil defense agency for information and enrollment forms.

To participate in RACES drills and exercises, you must be registered with your local civil defense organization. To avoid excessive use of Amateur frequencies, RACES drills are limited to one hour per week. Messages sent during a drill must be identified as simply tests so as not to unduly alarm the casual listener. (T2C04)(T2C05)(T2C06)

During the first stages of an emergency situation, the traffic is called **tactical communications**. In such cases, some of the more structured Amateur formats described in this book are modified. For example, one might use tactical call signs such as "command post," "hospital" or "weather center." (T2C07)

Most of the **traffic** (messages) in and out of a disaster area will relate to the status of people living in the area and affected by the situation. This is called *health and welfare* traffic. If the message relates to immediate safety of human life, it is called *emergency* traffic. (T2C08)

Would you like to configure your station to be ready in the case of a disaster? It can be easily accomplished. Let's say you have a two-meter base station in your bedroom. It probably operates from a 12-volt power supply connected to the commercial power lines. Of course, if the power fails, your rig is useless. However, you can continue to operate by connecting a 12-volt sealed (gel-cell) motorcycle battery across the DC leads of your AC power supply. If the commercial AC power fails, your two-meter rig will then draw power from the battery. Of course, if you have a handheld radio, you should have at least one spare battery and a way to charge it from the cigarette lighter jack powered by the automobile battery. (T2C10)(T2C11)

There is one other situation that can put you "out-of-business" in an emergency. Let's say you are caught in a hurricane. The chances are that your antenna will be blown down. You may be able to transmit with emergency power but the signal will not go anywhere without an antenna. It is an excellent idea to have a *dipole antenna* rolled up and stashed in the closet "just in case." Once the wind dies down, you can easily erect the antenna from whatever is left standing. A dipole will even work with a volunteer holding each insulated end in the air over their head! Remember, however, this is an emergency procedure. Normally you would not stand this close to an antenna RF field. (T2C12)

Novice Subelement 2 (2 questions)

N2A01—What should you do before you transmit on any frequency? (A) Listen to make sure others are not using the frequency; (B) Listen to make sure that someone will be able to hear you; (C) Check your antenna for resonance at the selected frequency; (D) Make sure the SWR on your antenna feed line is high enough.

N2A02—If you make contact with another station and your signal is extremely strong and perfectly readable, what adjustment might you make to your transmitter? (A) Turn on your speech processor; (B) Reduce you SWR; (C) Continue with your contact, making no changes; (D) Turn down your power output to the minimum necessary.

N2A03—What is one way to shorten transmitter tune-up time on the air to cut down on interference? (A) Use a random wire antenna; (B) Tune up on 40 meters first, then switch to the desired band; (C) Tune the transmitter into a dummy load; (D) Use twin lead instead of coaxial-cable feed lines.

N2A04—If you are in contact with another station and you hear an emergency call for help on your frequency, what should you do? (A) Tell the calling station that the frequency is in use; (B) Direct the calling station to the nearest emergency net frequency; (C) Call your local Civil Preparedness Office and inform them of the emergency; (D) Stop your QSO immediately and take the emergency call.

N2A05—What is the correct way to call CQ when using Morse code? (A) Send the letters "CQ" three times, followed by "DE," followed by your call sign sent once; (B) Send the letters "CQ" three times, followed by "DE," followed by your call sign sent three times; (C) Send the letters "CQ" ten times, followed by "DE," followed by your call sign sent once; (D) Send the letters "CQ" over and over.

N2A06—How should you answer a Morse code CQ call? (A) Send your call sign four times; (B) Send the other station's call sign twice, followed by "DE," followed by your call sign twice; (C) Send the other station's call sign once, followed by "DE," followed by your call sign four times; (D) Send your call sign followed by your name, station location and a signal report.

N2A07—At what speed should a Morse code CQ call be transmitted? (A) Only speeds below five WPM; (B) The highest speed your keyer will operate; (C) Any speed at which you can reliably receive; (D) The highest speed at which you can control the keyer.

N2A08—What is the meaning of the procedural signal "CQ"? (A) "Call on the quarter hour"; (B) "New antenna is being tested" (no station should answer); (C) "Only the called station should transmit"; (D) "Calling any station".

N2A09—What is the meaning of the procedural signal "DE"? (A) "From" or "this is," as in "W9NGT DE N9BTT"; (B) "Directional Emissions" from your antenna; (C) "Received all correctly"; (D) "Calling any station".

N2A10—What is the meaning of the procedural signal "K"? (A) "Any station transmit"; (B) "All received correctly"; (C) "End of message"; (D) "Called station only transmit".

N2A11—What is meant by the term "DX"? (A) Best regards; (B) Distant station; (C) Calling any station; (D) Go ahead.

N2A12—What is the meaning of the term "73"? (A) Long distance; (B) Best regards; (C) Love and kisses; (D) Go ahead.

N2A13—What are RST signal reports? (A) A short way to describe ionospheric conditions; (B) A short way to describe transmitter power; (C) A short way to describe signal reception; (D) A short way to describe sunspot activity.

N2A14—What does RST mean in a signal report? (A) Recovery, signal strength, tempo; (B) Recovery, signal speed, tone; (C) Readability, signal speed, tempo; (D) Readability, signal strength, tone.

N2A15—What is one meaning of the Q signal "QRS"? (A) Interference from static; (B) Send more slowly; (C) Send RST report; (D) Radio station location is.

N2A16—What is one meaning of the Q signal "QTH"? (A) Time here is; (B) My name is; (C) Stop sending; (D) My location is.

N2A17—What is a QSL card? (A) A letter or postcard from an Amateur pen pal; (B) A Notice of Violation from the FCC; (C) A written proof of communication between two Amateurs; (D) A postcard reminding you when your license will expire.

N2A18—What is the correct way to call CQ when using voice? (A) Say "CQ" once, followed by "this is," followed by your call sign spoken three times; (B) Say "CQ" at least five times, followed by "this is," followed by your call sign spoken once; (C) Say "CQ" three times, followed by "this is," followed by your call sign spoken three times; (D) Say "CQ" at least ten times, followed by "this is," followed by your call sign spoken once.

N2A19—How should you answer a voice CQ call? (A) Say the other station's call sign at least ten times, followed by "this is," then your call sign at least twice; (B) Say the other station's call sign at least five times phonetically, followed by "this is," then your call sign at least once; (C) Say the other station's call sign at least three times, followed by "this is," then your call sign at least five times phonetically; (D) Say the other station's call sign once, followed by "this is," then your call sign given phonetically.

N2A20—To make your call sign better understood when using voice transmissions, what should you do? (A) Use Standard International Phonetics for each letter of your call; (B) Use any words which start with the same letters as your call sign for each letter of your call; (C) Talk louder; (D) Turn up your microphone gain.

N2B01—What is the correct way to call CQ when using RTTY? (A) Send the letters "CQ" three times, followed by "DE," followed by your call sign sent once; (B) Send the letters "CQ" three to six times, followed by "DE," followed by your call sign sent three times; (C) Send the letters "CQ" ten times, followed by the procedural signal "DE", followed by your call sent one time; (D) Send the letters "CQ" over and over.

N2B02—What speed should you use when answering a CQ call using RTTY? (A) Half the speed of the received signal; (B) The same speed as the received signal; (C) Twice the speed of the received signal; (D) Any speed, since RTTY systems adjust to any signal speed.

N2B03—What does "connected" mean in a packet-radio link? (A) A telephone link is working between two stations; (B) A message has reached an Amateur station for local delivery; (C) A transmitting station is sending data to only one receiving station; it replies that the data is being received correctly; (D) A transmitting and receiving station are using a digipeater, so no other contacts can take place until they are finished.

N2B04—What does "monitoring" mean on a packet-radio frequency? (A) The FCC is copying all messages; (B) A member of the Amateur Auxiliary to the FCC's Field Operations Bureau is copying all messages; (C) A receiving station is displaying all messages sent to it, and replying that the messages are being received correctly; (D) A receiving station is displaying messages that may not be sent to it, and is not replying to any message.

N2B05—What is a digipeater? (A) A packet-radio station that retransmits only data that is marked to be retransmitted; (B) A packet-radio station that retransmits any data that it receives; (C) A repeater that changes audio signals to digital data; (D) A repeater built using only digital electronics parts.

N2B06—What does "network" mean in packet radio? (A) A way of connecting terminal-node controllers by telephone so data can be sent over long distances; (B) A way of connecting packet-radio stations so data can be sent over long distances; (C) The wiring connections on a terminal-node controller board; (D) The programming in a terminal-node controller that rejects other callers if a station is already connected.

N2B07—What is simplex operation? (A) Transmitting and receiving on the same frequency; (B) Transmitting and receiving over a wide area; (C) Transmitting on one frequency and receiving on another; (D) Transmitting one-way communications.

N2B08—When should you use simplex operation instead of a repeater? (A) When the most reliable communications are needed ; (B) When a contact is possible without using a repeater; (C) When an emergency telephone call is needed; (D) When you are traveling and need some local information.

N2B09—What is a good way to make contact on a repeater? (A) Say the call sign of the station you want to contact three times; (B) Say the other operator's name, then your call sign three times; (C) Say the call sign of the station you want to contact, then your call sign; (D) Say, "Breaker, breaker," then your call sign.

N2B10—When using a repeater to communicate, what do you need to know about the repeater besides its output frequency? (A) Its input frequency; (B) Its call sign; (C) Its power level; (D) Whether or not it has a phone patch.

N2B11—What is the main purpose of a repeater? (A) To make local information available 24 hours a day; (B) To link Amateur stations with the telephone system; (C) To retransmit NOAA weather information during severe storm warnings; (D) To increase the range of portable and mobile stations.

N2B12—What does it mean to say that a repeater has an input and an output frequency? (A) The repeater receives on one frequency and transmits on another; (B) The repeater offers a choice of operating frequency, in case one is busy; (C) One frequency is used to control the repeater and another is used to retransmit received signals; (D) The repeater must receive an access code on one frequency before retransmitting received signals.

N2B13—What is an autopatch? (A) Something that automatically selects the strongest signal to be repeated; (B) A device which connects a mobile station to the next repeater if it moves out of range of the first; (C) A device that allows repeater users to make telephone calls from their stations; (D) A device which locks other stations out of a repeater when there is an important conversation in progress.

N2B14—What is the purpose of a repeater time-out timer? (A) It lets a repeater have a rest period after heavy use; (B) It logs repeater transmit time to predict when a repeater will fail; (C) It tells how long someone has been using a repeater; (D) It limits the amount of time someone can transmit on a repeater.

N2B15—What is a CTCSS (or PL) tone? (A) A special signal used for telecommand control of model craft; (B) A sub-audible tone added to a carrier which may cause a receiver to accept a signal; (C) A tone used by repeaters to mark the end of a transmission; (D) A special signal used for telemetry between Amateur space stations and Earth stations

Technician Subelement 2 (3 questions)

T2A01—How do you call another station on a repeater if you know the station's call sign? (A) Say "break, break 79," then say the station's call sign; (B) Say the station's call sign, then identify your own station; (C) Say "CQ" three times, then say the station's call sign; (D) Wait for the station to call "CQ," then answer it.

T2A02—Why should you pause briefly between transmissions when using a repeater? (A) To check the SWR of the repeater; (B) To reach for pencil and paper for third-party communications; (C) To listen for anyone wanting to break in; (D) To dial up the repeater's autopatch.

T2A03—Why should you keep transmissions short when using a repeater? (A) A long transmission may prevent someone with an emergency from using the repeater; (B) To see if the receiving station operator is still awake; (C) To give any listening non-hams a chance to respond; (D) To keep long distance charges down.

T2A04—What is the proper way to break into a conversation on a repeater? (A) Wait for the end of a transmission and start calling the desired party; (B) Shout, "break, break!" to show that you're eager to join the conversation; (C) Turn on an amplifier and override whoever is talking; (D) Say your call sign during a break between transmissions.

T2A05—What is the purpose of repeater operation? (A) To cut your power bill by using someone else's higher power system; (B) To help mobile and low-power stations extend their usable range; (C) To transmit signals for observing propagation and reception; (D) To make calls to stores more than 50 miles away.

T2A06—What causes a repeater to "time out"? (A) The repeater's battery supply runs out; (B) Someone's transmission goes on longer than the repeater allows; (C) The repeater gets too hot and stops transmitting until its circuitry cools off; (D) Something is wrong with the repeater.

T2A07—During commuting rush hours, which type of repeater operation should be discouraged? (A) Mobile stations; (B) Low-power stations; (C) Highway traffic information nets; (D) Third-party communications nets.

T2A08—What is a courtesy tone (used in repeater operations)? (A) A sound used to identify the repeater; (B) A sound used to indicate when a transmission is complete; (C) A sound used to indicate that a message is waiting for someone; (D) A sound used to activate a receiver in case of severe weather.

T2A09—What is the meaning of: "Your signal is full quieting..."? (A) Your signal is strong enough to overcome all receiver noise; (B) Your signal has no spurious sounds; (C) Your signal is not strong enough to be received; (D) Your signal is being received, but no audio is being heard.

T2A10—How should you give a signal report over a repeater? (A) Say what your receiver's S-meter reads; (B) Always say: "Your signal report is five five..."; (C) Say the amount of signal quieting into the repeater; (D) Try to imitate the sound quality you are receiving.

T2A11—What is a repeater called which is available for anyone to use? (A) An open repeater; (B) A closed repeater; (C) An autopatch repeater; (D) A private repeater.

T2A12—What is the usual input/output frequency separation for repeaters in the 2-meter band? (A) 600 kHz; (B) 1.0 MHz; (C) 1.6 MHz; (D) 5.0 MHz.

T2A13—What is the usual input/output frequency separation for repeaters in the 1.25-meter band? (A) 600 kHz; (B) 1.0 MHz; (C) 1.6 MHz; (D) 5.0 MHz.

T2A14—What is the usual input/output frequency separation for repeaters in the 70-centimeter band? (A) 600 kHz; (B) 1.0 MHz; (C) 1.6 MHz; (D) 5.0 MHz.

T2A15—Why should local Amateur communications use VHF and UHF frequencies instead of HF frequencies? (A) To minimize interference on HF bands capable of long distance communication; (B) Because greater output power is permitted on VHF and UHF; (C) Because HF transmissions are not propagated locally; (D) Because signals are louder on VHF and UHF frequencies.

T2A16—How might you join a closed repeater system? (A) Contact the control operator and ask to join; (B) Use the repeater until told not to; (C) Use simplex on the repeater input until told not to; (D) Write the FCC and report the closed condition.

T2A17—How can on-the-air interference be minimized during a lengthy transmitter testing or loading up procedure? (A) Choose an unoccupied frequency; (B) Use a dummy load; (C) Use a non-resonant antenna; (D) Use a resonant antenna that requires no loading-up procedure.

T2A18—What is the proper way to ask someone their location when using a repeater? (A) What is your QTH; (B) What is your 20; (C) Where are you; (D) Locations are not normally told by radio.

T2B01—Why should simplex be used where possible, instead of using a repeater? (A) Signal range will be increased; (B) Long distance toll charges will be avoided; (C) The repeater will not be tied up unnecessarily; (D) Your antenna's effectiveness will be better tested.

T2B02—If you are talking to a station using a repeater, how would you find out if you could communicate using simplex instead? (A) See if you can clearly receive the station on the repeater's input frequency; (B) See if you can clearly receive the station on a lower frequency band; (C) See if you can clearly receive a more distant repeater; (D) See if a third station can clearly receive both of you.

T2B03—If you are operating simplex on a repeater frequency, why would it be good Amateur practice to change to another frequency? (A) The repeater's output power may ruin your station's receiver; (B) There are more repeater operators than simplex operators; (C) Changing the repeater's frequency is not practical; (D) Changing the repeater's frequency requires the authorization of the FCC.

T2B04—What is a repeater frequency coordinator? (A) Someone who organizes the assembly of a repeater station; (B) Someone who provides advice on what kind of repeater to buy; (C) The person whose call sign is used for a repeater's identification; (D) A person or group that recommends frequencies for repeater usage.

T2B05—What is the proper Q signal to use to see if a frequency is in use before transmitting on CW? (A) QRV?; (B) QRU?; (C) QRL?; (D) QRZ?.

T2B06—What is one meaning of the Q signal "QSY"? (A) Change frequency; (B) Send more slowly; (C) Send faster; (D) Use more power.

T2B07—What is one meaning of the Q signal "QSO"? (A) A contact is confirmed; (B) A conversation is in progress; (C) A contact is ending; (D) A conversation is desired.

T2B08—What is the proper Q signal to use to ask if someone is calling you on CW? (A) QSL?; (B) QRZ?; (C) QRL?; (D) QRT?.

T2B09—What is the meaning of: "Your signal report is five seven..."? (A) Your signal is perfectly readable and moderately strong; (B) Your signal is perfectly readable, but weak; (C) Your signal is readable with considerable difficulty; (D) Your signal is perfectly readable with near pure tone.

T2B10—What is the meaning of: "Your signal report is three three..."? (A) The contact is serial number thirty-three; (B) The station is located at latitude 33 degrees; (C) Your signal is readable with considerable difficulty and weak in strength; (D) Your signal is unreadable, very weak in strength.

T2B11—What is the meaning of: "Your signal report is five nine plus 20 dB..."? (A) Your signal strength has increased by a factor of 100; (B) Repeat your transmission on a frequency 20 kHz higher; (C) The bandwidth of your signal is 20 decibels above linearity; (D) A relative signal-strength meter reading is 20 decibels greater than strength 9.

T2C01—What is the proper distress call to use when operating phone? (A) Say "MAYDAY" several times; (B) Say "HELP" several times; (C) Say "EMERGENCY" several times; (D) Say "SOS" several times.

T2C02—What is the proper distress call to use when operating CW? (A) MAYDAY; (B) QRRR; (C) QRZ; (D) SOS.

T2C03—What is the proper way to interrupt a repeater conversation to signal a distress call? (A) Say "BREAK" twice, then your call sign; (B) Say "HELP" as many times as it takes to get someone to answer; (C) Say "SOS," then your call sign; (D) Say "EMERGENCY" three times.

T2C04—With what organization must you register before you can participate in RACES drills? (A) A local Amateur Radio club; (B) A local racing organization; (C) The responsible civil defense organization; (D) The Federal Communications Commission.

T2C05—What is the maximum number of hours allowed per week for RACES drills? (A) One; (B) Six, but not more than one hour per day; (C) Eight; (D) As many hours as you want.

T2C06—How must you identify messages sent during a RACES drill? (A) As emergency messages; (B) As Amateur traffic; (C) As official government messages; (D) As drill or test messages.

T2C07—What is one reason for using tactical call signs such as "command post" or "weather center" during an emergency? (A) They keep the general public informed about what is going on; (B) They are more efficient and help coordinate public-service communications; (C) They are required by the FCC; (D) They increase goodwill between Amateurs.

T2C08—What type of messages concerning a person's well-being are sent into or out of a disaster area? (A) Routine traffic; (B) Tactical traffic; (C) Formal message traffic; (D) Health and Welfare traffic.

T2C09—What are messages called which are sent into or out of a disaster area concerning the immediate safety of human life? (A) Tactical traffic; (B) Emergency traffic; (C) Formal message traffic; (D) Health and Welfare traffic.

T2C10—Why is it a good idea to have a way to operate your Amateur station without using commercial AC power lines? (A) So you may use your station while mobile; (B) So you may provide communications in an emergency; (C) So you may operate in contests where AC power is not allowed; (D) So you will comply with the FCC rules.

T2C11—What is the most important accessory to have for a hand held radio in an emergency? (A) An extra antenna; (B) A portable amplifier; (C) Several sets of charged batteries; (D) A microphone headset for hands-free operation.

T2C12—Which type of antenna would be a good choice as part of a portable HF Amateur station that could be set up in case of an emergency? (A) A three-element quad; (B) A three-element Yagi; (C) A dipole; (D) A parabolic dish.

Chapter

3

Radio Propagation

This is a "fun" chapter. It discusses a number of interesting aspects of how radio signals get from one place to another. Much of the information in this chapter is not required knowledge to pass the Technician test. Hopefully you found the subject interesting and informative. The questions are easy, too. You will be asked only one question from the Novice pool and three from the Technician pool.

The "Exciting" World of Ham Radio

How does one Amateur communicate with another? By means of invisible waves which are radiated from an antenna connected to a transmitter. The radio frequency (RF) energy produced by the transmitter travels up to the antenna via one or more wires called a **transmission line**. The antenna accepts this energy and uses it to excite the environment surrounding the antenna.

True enough, but why can't one talk a thousand miles on a handheld transceiver? How is it possible to hear stations from thousands of miles away on a portable shortwave receiver? Clearly, there's a lot more going on here than the previous paragraph would seem to indicate.

Exciting the environment is a confusing concept and it doesn't mean shaking your "booty" at the disco! We cannot see, feel or hear this "excitation." Even so, we know there is a coupling between the antenna and the space surrounding it.

Ham Radio Billiards

You can think of the radio frequency excitation as an almost endless series of atomic-sized billiard balls. They stretch out from the antenna in all directions and pass the excitation along by clicking ball-to-ball. No single ball moves very far but the energy is imparted ball-to-ball. This continues until the balls either run out of energy or bang into another antenna.

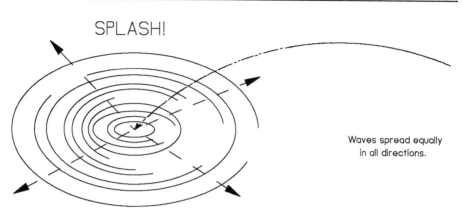

SPLASH!

Waves spread equally
in all directions.

Figure 3-1 There are analogies between water action and radio signals. When a rock is thrown in a pool, the waves act like alternating current.

When our imaginary billiard balls reach another antenna, they induce a weak voltage in it. The receiver connected to the antenna converts the tiny signal back into the original information.

Many volts of radio frequency energy will be delivered to and radiated by a transmitting antenna. Only a few millionths of a volt will be induced in the receiving antenna. Obviously banging all those billiard balls around dissipates a lot of energy!

The billiard balls are actually electrons that vibrate and pass along their energy (see *Chapter 5*). The electrical signal that radiates from the antenna does so in undulations similar to waves traveling across water. If you could, by magic, make the waves visible, you would see ripples spreading out from the antenna very much as if you had thrown a pebble into a still pond (see *Figure 3-1*). The waves would radiate out in concentric circles consisting of a series of crests and valleys. Near the impact point of the pebble (the antenna), the waves would be strongest. They would diminish in strength as they traveled across the water.

If the pond was not too wide and the force of the thrown pebble was sufficient, the waves might make an impact on the shore. The size of the pebble and the force accompanying it, represent the transmitter **power**. The water surface, and the loss of strength resulting from trying to move the water, represents **resistance**.

Amplitude, Wavelength and Frequency

Radio signals are somewhat like the wave action when a pebble is thrown into a quiet pool of water. The ripples radiate from the point of impact (where the pebble hit) in concentric circles.

As the first wave reaches the shore, the water level rises. Then as the crest passes, the water level drops to its original or normal position. But as the wave continues across the pond, the crest is followed by a trough. This causes the water level to drop below

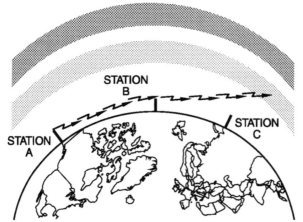

Figure 3-2 VHF signals travel in a straight line. They can be intercepted by an antenna which is close but will pass above (and not heard by) a distant reception point.

its original position. This action repeats until the wave action runs out of energy and the pond returns to its original still condition. The complete action from normal, crest, normal, valley, normal is our old friend the *sine wave*.

There are three characteristics of a sine wave that you should be aware of. They are the (1) *amplitude*, (2) *wavelength*, and (3) *frequency*. The vertical distance between the crest and the trough is the **amplitude** of the wave. The bigger the rock, the larger the amplitude of the wave. If you toss a Volkswagen in the quiet pool, larger waves will be created than for a small pebble.

The distance between any two reference points (for example between two crests or two troughs) is the length of the wave or, more commonly, the **wavelength**. The number of times a crest (or a valley) passes a given point *in a specific length of time* is called the **frequency**. These repetitive cycles must be related to time. The most common unit of time is the second. Thus, frequency is expressed in the number of cycles per second (actually Hertz per second or simply Hz).

You should be able to visualize the relationship between frequency and wavelength. As frequency is increased, wavelength decreases. Conversely, as wavelength increases, the frequency of the wave must decrease.

Remember, the number of sine wave events which occur each second is referred to as the frequency. The distance or length between any two identical and repetitive reference points on a sine wave is called the wavelength.

VHF and UHF Signals Go Straight

Chapter 2 presented a simple chart of the various radio frequencies. The section also described the characteristics of Amateur bands on which the Novice and Technician licensee are permitted to operate. You will recall there was a remarkable difference in the communication range between 10 meters (HF) and the 3/4 meter (UHF) band.

With a couple of exceptions, VHF and UHF signals are relatively undisturbed by external forces. For examples, signals radiated by the antenna of a handheld transceiver travel by *direct waves in a straight line* and are intercepted by a distant antenna. Contrary to what the "Flat Earth Society" believes, the earth is round. Since the signals do not bend around the earth, they will pass high over your head (and your antenna) if your receiving location is too far distant from the transmitting point. This is called **line-of-sight** communication. In other words, if the antennas can "see" each other, the radio stations connected to the antennas can communicate. This effect is illustrated in *Figure 3-2*. (N3A01)(N3A02)(N3A03)(N3C03)

What are the exceptions mentioned above? Well for one, VHF signals are easily *reflected*. It is not at all unusual for two distant VHF stations to communicate with each other with the help of a mountain. If the Amateurs were to point their directional antennas at each other, most of the signal strength might pass overhead and be lost in space. However, by pointing their antennas at a mutually visible mountain, enough signal is reflected between stations to permit communications. In the city, metal framed buildings are excellent reflectors of VHF signals. (N3A04)

High Frequency Signals—Predictably Unpredictable

The transmission or propagation of signals on the high frequency (HF) bands (3-30 MHz) is fascinating. Unlike VHF, HF signals are almost completely influenced by external factors.

The energy which departs the HF antenna actually has two components, the **sky wave** and the **ground wave**. The ground wave "slithers" electronically along the surface of the earth. It is dissipated within a few miles of the transmitter due to the resistance it encounters from the dry earth. Because of this, working *distant stations* solely by means of the ground wave is actually quite difficult. The sky wave travels many times further and can even reach foreign countries if they are beyond each others skip zone (see *Figure 3-3*). (N3A05)(N3A06)

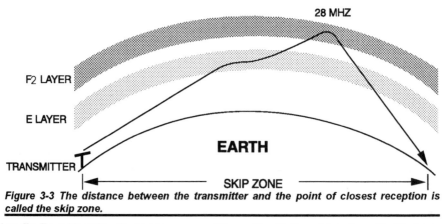

Figure 3-3 The distance between the transmitter and the point of closest reception is called the skip zone.

Ultraviolet rays from the sun beam down on the earth each day. The excitation of ions and free electrons in gasses high above the earth by the sun causes them to be **ionized**. The effect of the sun is called **ionization**. The sun's rays excite the electrons in the ionosphere, causing them to behave in a strange way. When the excitation is high enough, radio signals which strike the ionosphere can be repelled or "reflected" back to earth at a point far distant from their origin. This signal bending is called **ionospheric refraction.** (N3A08)(N3A10)(T3A01)(T3A02)(T3A03)(T3A04)

During the night the free electrons dissipate. Thus the *minimum ionization level occurs just before dawn.* The ionosphere absorbs radiation very quickly. By *noon* the ionization reaches a *maximum.* This does not mean that this is the best time to communicate over long distances. Remember that the ionosphere has to be percolating along *at both ends of the circuit.* Thus the best time for DX'ing is *right after dawn and just before sunset.* (T3B05)(T3B06)(T3B07)

This is what causes the difference in characteristics between HF and VHF. The ionosphere, well above the atmosphere, contains enough *ions and free electrons* that it is capable of refracting high frequency signals. Signals transmitted via this medium are called **sky-wave communications.** (N3A07)

For the most part, VHF signals are not affected by the ionosphere and pass straight through. If this were not the case, we would be unable to communicate with our satellites which orbit above the ionosphere and travel to other planetary systems.

Although we cannot see the ionosphere, we can certainly observe and describe its effects. The ionosphere acts very much like an **electronic mirror** which reflects radio signals back to earth at some distant point. Unfortunately the "mirror" is not as consistent as the one you stare at each morning. The ionosphere is constantly in motion and in a state of turmoil. The "reflectability" varies from transparent to nearly perfect. It can also move up and down, thereby increasing or decreasing the angle of the

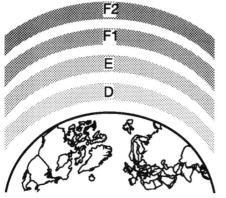

Figure 3-4 The ionosphere layers actually merge and are not distinct, as shown here.

signals bounced back to earth (and therefore the impact point). We refer to those signals which are reflected by the ionosphere as **skip transmissions**. The signals actually leave the surface of the earth and are bent (or refracted) by the ionosphere. They arrive back at the earth's surface at some distance from the point of origin.

Between the transmission and reception point, the signal cannot be received. The ground wave has long since dissipated. This area of no reception is called the **skip zone** and is shown in *Figure 3-3*. Typically, the 10-meter skip zone is 500-1,000 miles but can be considerably shorter or longer under unusual conditions. (N3A09)

While we cannot see the ionosphere, we think it looks something like the drawing in *Figure 3-4*. Actually, the sketch is a little misleading. There are no distinct layers like a Jello desert. Rather, one layer blends into the next. The regions are labeled **D, E, F1** and **F2** because certain layers of the ionosphere have different characteristics. Some layers influence the lower frequencies. For example, the ionized D layer (the closest to the earth) peaks at midday. This limits daytime longwave communications (such as 80-meters) to short distances due to *absorption of the energy*. The D-layer is the least useful for long distance radio propagation. (T3A05)(T3A06)(T3A08) (T3B01) (T3B02)(T3B03) (T3B04)(T3B08)(T3C09)

The E layer is the lowest region that is useful for long distance propagation. It also creates erratic propagation conditions at the upper end of the HF spectrum and lower end of the very high frequency spectrum (six meters). When this occurs, it is called **sporadic-E**. One indication of sporadic-E is the reception of stations normally in the skip zone (500-600 miles away) of 10 meters. (T3A07)(T3C11)

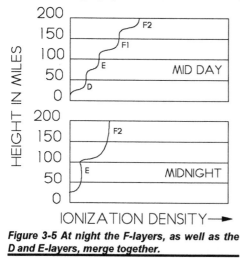

The F layers (F1 and F2) are capable of supporting worldwide communications on a consistent basis. The F2 layer is mainly responsible for long distance sky-wave communications. At night the F1 and F2 layers combine as shown in *Figure 3-5*. (T3A09)(T3A10) (T3A11)

Figure 3-5 At night the F-layers, as well as the D and E-layers, merge together.

Nature's Acne—The Sunspots

The ionosphere is highly charged by particles from the sun. This explains why the characteristics of radio signals are different between day and night. But what explains the reason the ionosphere sometimes goes "bonkers"?

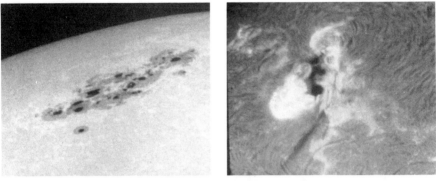

Two views of sunspots taken by cameras mounted in high altitude rockets.

The sun exhibits a cyclic condition in which **sunspots** appear on the surface. The action of the sun over this period is called the **sunspot cycle**. Approximately every *11 years*, these solar "pimples" reach a peak as shown in *Figure 3-6*. For two or three years on either side of the peak, all heck breaks loose in the HF portion of the radio spectrum due to the high level of radiation of the ionosphere.(N3A11)(N3A12)

Occasionally one of the sunspots erupts into a solar flare. Electrons shower the earth like an oil leak from an old Volkswagen. When this occurs, the ionosphere blows its chromosomes and becomes paralyzed at all frequencies. This can completely disrupt radio communications circuits and cause radio "blackouts". The intensity of the solar radiation can even disrupt telephone cables lying on the ocean floor! The blackout can last for hours or days, depending on the intensity and duration of the flare. During the Spring of 1990, Amateurs experienced a total blackout of the 10-meter band, even though we were at a peak in the sunspot cycle. The ionization level was so high that 10-meter signals were absorbed, rather than being passed or reflected, by the ionosphere.

Sunspots are magnetic field blemishes on the surface of the sun which can be observed and photographed. The spots seem to be directly related with how much radiation strikes the ionosphere and its level of ionization.

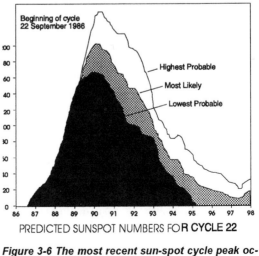

PREDICTED SUNSPOT NUMBERS FOR CYCLE 22

Figure 3-6 The most recent sun-spot cycle peak occurred in early 1991.

The fact that the sun plays such an important part in the functioning of the ionosphere also causes a number of associated phenomena. The seasons will affect propagation differently. Usually distant signals are much stronger in the Winter than in the Summer. Just the opposite is true for sporadic-E, which accounts for the reception of distant television stations in the summer.

The ionosphere of the northern hemisphere reacts differently from that of the southern hemisphere, since their seasons are opposite. Some radio conditions will improve at night, while on other bands the signals will disappear altogether. No doubt you've heard broadcast stations coming in from great distances on your car radio. This usually happens at night during the Winter. In the southern hemisphere, the effect is most noticeable in the Summer.

Is This Band "Open For Business"

The ionosphere has some of the properties of a photographic filter. Some of the "colors" (frequencies) will pass through, while others will be absorbed or reflected.

The ionization level determines how high a frequency will be reflected by the ionosphere. The more sunspots there are, the greater the ionization. By observing the onset of the spots near the sun's rim, we can predict what radio conditions will be like in the following weeks.

If we were to beam signals of an increasingly higher frequency at the ionosphere, they would be reflected farther and farther from their origin. Finally, a point where reflection no longer occurs would be reached. At this point, the angle would be so sharp and the ionization level sufficiently low that reflection can no longer occur. Above this critical point, signals will pass through the ionosphere and be lost forever in space as illustrated in *Figure 3-7*.(T3B09)

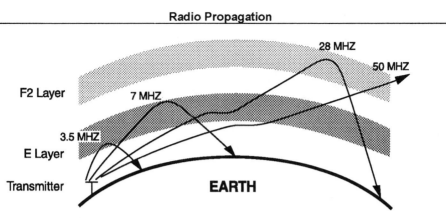

Figure 3-7 The Maximum Usable Frequency (MUF) is somewhere between 28 and 50 MHz in this drawing.

The highest or **critical frequency** which can be reflected by the ionosphere is called the **maximum usable frequency** or **MUF**. This is defined as the highest frequency that will be bent back to the earth. As the amount of solar radiation reaching the earth varies, so does the MUF. (T3B10)(T3B11)

During periods of peak solar activity, MUF can reach 50 MHz or higher. When the MUF gets this high, the ol' ionosphere really gets swinging like a Jai alai champion. World-wide communication becomes commonplace on the 10-meter band and even occurs on the 6 meters (50 MHz). It is not at all unusual to work European or Asian stations from your car on 10 meters during these peaks. The current peak in sunspot activity occurred in Winter of 1990 or early in 1991.

One might think that the MUF would drop to a very low value at night when the sun is illuminating the other side of the earth. Fortunately, this is not the case. Usually at night the F layers merge together, as do the D and E layers. Dr. Van Allen's satellite experiments discovered a radiation doughnut around the earth (the Van Allen belt). The belt follows the earth's magnetic lines of force and serves to trap solar radiation in its electronic spider web. As a result, ionization can continue long after the sun has set. Because of the Van Allen belt, ionization will be minimal at the earth's poles and maximum near the equator. This accounts for the fact that we hear a preponderance of Central and South American stations when the skip really starts coming in.

Other Propagation Modes

Sporadic-E—Occasionally "hot spots" develop in the ionosphere around the E layer. This effect is stronger in the summer months, while longer distance (because it is higher) F layer propagation is stronger in the Winter. These hot patches of ionosphere are called sporadic-E and may be only a few hundred miles across. Between any two points that are able to bounce a signal off the hotspot, extremely strong signal strengths can occur. The MUF for the path can actually double due to this invisible ionized cloud. When sporadic-E hits, it is not at all unusual to have contacts with South America on the six-meter (50 MHz) Amateur band. On 10 meters you may hear the band open up suddenly to a specific area and then, sometime later, shut down just as quickly as it started. This is the effect of sporadic-E.

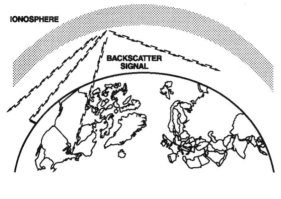

Scatter—As we've seen, the ionosphere is not a smooth continuous surface. Some radiation will scatter at angles that reach stations *within a skip zone*. The signals will be *weak and hollow sounding* but if the stations have enough power and interference is low, they can hear each other. This mode is called "scatter communications." (T3C01)(T3C02)

Figure 3-8 Signals striking the ionosphere will be "scattered" weakly back toward the source, in addition to being reflected toward distant stations.

Backscatter—Like the scatter mode mentioned previously, the ionosphere can reflect signals back toward the source of the transmission. When calling DX, several Amateurs may have their directional antennas pointed toward the DX station. Since the antennas are pointed in the same general direction, it is possible for stations within a skip zone to hear each other. This mode is called **backscatter propagation** and is illustrated in *Figure 3-8*. Backscatter reception sounds much the same as scatter communications.

Tropospheric Propagation—DX communication is actually possible on VHF which is normally line-of-sight. The effect is called **atmospheric ducting** or **tropospheric propagation**. How does DX on VHF happen? Occasionally, when a stable high pressure system (a layer of cool air) stalls over an area of warm air, the *temperature inversion* acts as a "pipe" or duct for *VHF radio signals*. Many Southern California Amateurs have communicated on two meters with Hawaii via widespread temperature inversions over the ocean. An example of this is shown in *Figure 3-9*. (T3C04)(T3C05)(T3C06) (T2C07)(T3C08)(T3C10)

On this, and the following pages, you will find the questions relating to propagation and what happens to emissions when they travel from one place to another.

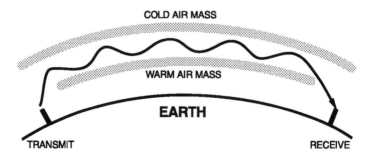

Figure 3-9 Large warm air masses can actually function like a "waveguide" to bend VHF signals around the curvature of the earth.

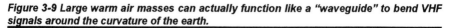

Novice Subelement 3 (1 question)

N3A01—When a signal travels in a straight line from one antenna to another, what is this called? (A) Line-of-sight propagation; (B) Straight-line propagation; (C) Knife-edge diffraction; (D) Tunnel propagation.

N3A02—What type of propagation usually occurs from one hand held VHF transceiver to another nearby? (A) Tunnel propagation; (B) Sky-wave propagation; (C) Line-of-sight propagation; (D) Auroral propagation.

N3A03—How do VHF and UHF radio waves usually travel from a transmitting antenna to a receiving antenna? (A) They bend through the ionosphere; (B) They go in a straight line; (C) They wander in any direction; (D) They move in a circle going either east or west from the transmitter.

N3A04—What can happen to VHF or UHF signals going towards a metal-framed building? (A) They will go around the building; (B) They can be bent by the ionosphere; (C) They can be easily reflected by the building; (D) They are sometimes scattered in the ectosphere.

N3A05—When a signal travels along the surface of the Earth, what is this called? (A) Sky-wave propagation; (B) Knife-edge diffraction; (C) E-region propagation; (D) Ground-wave propagation.

N3A06—How does the range of sky-wave propagation compare to ground-wave propagation? (A) It is much shorter; (B) It is much longer; (C) It is about the same; (D) It depends on the weather.

N3A07—When a signal is returned to earth by the ionosphere, what is this called? (A) Sky-wave propagation; (B) Earth-moon-earth propagation; (C) Ground-wave propagation; (D) Tropospheric propagation.

N3A08—What is the usual cause of sky-wave propagation? (A) Signals are reflected by a mountain; (B) Signals are reflected by the moon; (C) Signals are bent back to earth by the ionosphere; (D) Signals are repeated by a repeater.

N3A09—What is a skip zone? (A) An area covered by ground-wave propagation; (B) An area covered by sky-wave propagation; (C) An area which is too far away for ground-wave propagation, but too close for sky-wave propagation; (D) An area which is too far away for ground-wave or sky-wave propagation.

N3A10—What are the regions of ionized gases high above the earth called? (A) The ionosphere; (B) The troposphere; (C) The gas region; (D) The ion zone.

N3A11—How do sunspots change the ionization of the atmosphere? (A) The more sunspots there are, the greater the ionization; (B) The more sunspots there are, the less the ionization; (C) Unless there are sunspots, the ionization is zero; (D) They have no effect.

N3A12—How long is an average sunspot cycle? (A) 2 years; (B) 5 years; (C) 11 years; (D) 17 years

Technician Subelement 3 (3 questions)

T3A01—What is the ionosphere? (A) An area of the outer atmosphere where enough ions and free electrons exist to propagate radio waves; (B) An area between two air masses of different temperature and humidity, along which radio waves can travel; (C) An ionized path in the atmosphere where lightning has struck; (D) An area of the atmosphere where weather takes place.

T3A02—What is the name of the area that makes long-distance radio communications possible by bending radio waves? (A) Troposphere; (B) Stratosphere; (C) Magneto-sphere; (D) Ionosphere.

T3A03—What causes the ionosphere to form? (A) Solar radiation ionizing the outer atmosphere; (B) Temperature changes ionizing the outer atmosphere; (C) Lightning ionizing the outer atmosphere; (D) Release of fluorocarbons into the atmosphere.

T3A04—What type of solar radiation is most responsible for ionization in the outer atmosphere? (A) Thermal; (B) Ionized particle; (C) Ultraviolet; (D) Microwave.

T3A05—Which ionospheric region limits daytime radio communications on the 80-meter band to short distances? (A) D region; (B) E region; (C) F1 region; (D) F2 region.

T3A06—Which ionospheric region is closest to the earth? (A) The A region; (B) The D region; (C) The E region; (D) The F region.

T3A07—Which ionospheric region most affects sky-wave propagation on the 6-meter band? (A) The D region; (B) The E region; (C) The F1 region; (D) The F2 region.

T3A08—Which region of the ionosphere is the least useful for long-distance radio wave propagation? (A) The D region; (B) The E region; (C) The F1 region; (D) The F2 region.

T3A09—Which region of the ionosphere is mainly responsible for long-distance sky-wave radio communications? (A) D region; (B) E region; (C) F1 region; (D) F2 region.

T3A10—What two sub-regions of ionosphere exist only in the daytime? (A) Troposphere and stratosphere; (B) F1 and F2; (C) Electrostatic and electromagnetic; (D) D and E.

T3A11—Which two daytime ionospheric regions combine into one region at night? (A) E and F1; (B) D and E; (C) F1 and F2; (D) E1 and E2.

T3B01—Which region of the ionosphere is mainly responsible for absorbing radio signals during the daytime? (A) The F2 region; (B) The F1 region; (C) The E region; (D) The D region.

T3B02—When does ionospheric absorption of radio signals occur? (A) When tropospheric ducting occurs; (B) When long wavelength signals enter the D region; (C) When signals travel to the F region; (D) When a temperature inversion occurs.

T3B03—What effect does the D region of the ionosphere have on lower-frequency HF signals in the daytime? (A) It absorbs the signals; (B) It bends the radio waves out into space; (C) It refracts the radio waves back to earth; (D) It has little or no effect on 80-meter radio waves.

T3B04—What causes the ionosphere to absorb radio waves? (A) The weather below the ionosphere; (B) The ionization of the D region; (C) The presence of ionized clouds in the E region; (D) The splitting of the F region.

T3B05—What is the condition of the ionosphere just before local sunrise? (A) Atmospheric attenuation is at a maximum; (B) The D region is above the E region; (C) The E region is above the F region; (D) Ionization is at a minimum.

T3B06—When is the ionosphere most ionized? (A) Dusk; (B) Midnight; (C) Midday; (D) Dawn.

T3B07—When is the ionosphere least ionized? (A) Shortly before dawn; (B) Just after noon; (C) Just after dusk; (D) Shortly before midnight.

T3B08—When is the E region most ionized? (A) Dawn; (B) Midday; (C) Dusk; (D) Midnight.

T3B09—What happens to signals higher in frequency than the critical frequency? (A) They pass through the ionosphere; (B) They are absorbed by the ionosphere; (C) Their frequency is changed by the ionosphere to be below the maximum usable frequency; (D) They are reflected back to their source.

T3B10—What causes the maximum usable frequency to vary? (A) The temperature of the ionosphere; (B) The speed of the winds in the upper atmosphere; (C) The amount of radiation received from the sun, mainly ultraviolet; (D) The type of weather just below the ionosphere.

T3B11—What does maximum usable frequency mean? (A) The highest frequency signal that is bent back to the earth; (B) The lowest frequency signal that is bent back to the earth; (C) The highest frequency signal that is most absorbed by the ionosphere; (D) The lowest frequency signal that is most absorbed by the ionosphere.

T3C01—What kind of propagation would best be used by two stations within each other's skip zone on a certain frequency? (A) Ground-wave; (B) Sky-wave; (C) Scatter-mode; (D) Ducting.

T3C02—If you are receiving a weak and distorted signal from a distant station on a frequency close to the maximum usable frequency, what type of propagation is probably occurring? (A) Ducting; (B) Line-of-sight; (C) Scatter; (D) Ground-wave.

T3C03—How are VHF signals propagated within the range of the visible horizon? (A) By sky wave; (B) By direct wave; (C) By plane wave; (D) By geometric wave.

T3C04—Ducting occurs in which region of the atmosphere? (A) F2; (B) Ectosphere; (C) Troposphere; (D) Stratosphere.

T3C05—What effect does tropospheric bending have on 2-meter radio waves? (A) It lets you contact stations farther away; (B) It causes them to travel shorter distances; (C) It garbles the signal; (D) It reverses the sideband of the signal.

T3C06—What causes tropospheric ducting of radio waves? (A) A very low pressure area; (B) An aurora to the north; (C) Lightning between the transmitting and receiving stations; (D) A temperature inversion.

T3C07—What causes VHF radio waves to be propagated several hundred miles over oceans? (A) A polar air mass; (B) A widespread temperature inversion; (C) An overcast of cirriform clouds; (D) A high-pressure zone.

T3C08—In what frequency range does tropospheric ducting most often occur? (A) SW; (B) MF; (C) HF; (D) VHF.

T3C09—In what frequency range does sky-wave propagation least often occur? (A) LF; (B) MF; (C) HF; (D) VHF.

T3C10—What weather condition may cause tropospheric ducting? (A) A stable high-pressure system; (B) An unstable low-pressure system; (C) A series of low-pressure waves; (D) Periods of heavy rainfall.

T3C11—What band conditions might indicate long-range skip on the 6-meter and 2-meter bands? (A) Noise on the 80-meter band; (B) The absence of signals on the 10-meter band; (C) Very long-range skip on the 10-meter band; (D) Strong signals on the 10-meter band from stations about 500-600 miles away.

Chapter

4

Amateur Radio Practice

To see if you understand safety and good practice, you will be asked four questions from Subelement 2D and four questions from the Subelement 3AD question pool.

Safety First

Hobbies are generally rather benign. One might cut a lip while licking a stamp hinge or get a bruised ankle from a runaway RC model car. Unless you collect dangerous snakes or navigate hot air balloons, your hobby probably does not involve personal safety.

Amateur Radio is not a benign hobby. But don't get the impression that it is a dangerous hobby, either. However, there are a number of areas where care must be exercised to avoid harmful situations.

Antennas and Towers

All too often we hear of an unfortunate Amateur who, in erecting an antenna, comes in contact with power lines and is electrocuted. Everything seems to be under control, then someone loses their grip or stumbles, the tower falls and poof!

Some thoughtless Amateurs do not wear a **safety belt** (in good condition!) when climbing an antenna tower. Seldom a year goes by without a ham falling and breaking bones, or worse. It seems so simple, but up about the 40-foot level of the tower, Harry Ham's high blood pressure kicks in, he gets a little dizzy and loses his grip. Presto—he is transported to the emergency entrance of the local hospital for treatment of multiple broken bones. (N4B09)

You would be surprised at the number of hams, working under an antenna, who get "beaned" by wrenches and screwdrivers. Hams are pretty "thick-skulled" but a

Philips screwdriver traveling at 40 miles an hour makes a very effective arrow. One should always wear a **hard-hat** and **safety glasses** in any area where there is any possibility of falling objects. It has nothing to do with macho—it has to do with "smarts". (N4B08)(N4B11)

Practice Safe Service

Most Amateur equipment today is all solid state and operates from a 12-volt DC power supply. A ham rig seldom presents a serious safety hazard except for the occasional RF burn from an antenna. Since this can happen, an antenna should be mounted high enough that a person cannot touch it.

RF burns are painful, but seldom lethal, since radio frequency energy travels on the surface of objects (including the human body). Thus the energy is not able to reach the heart and paralyze the muscles which keep it pumping. Even so, radio frequency energy can be very dangerous. Not only can it burn and cook you, but evidence indicates there may be harmful long-term effects of exposure to radio frequency energy. We'll look at some of the dangers of RF shortly.

Amateur high power radio frequency amplifiers can legally deliver 1500 watts of power. Most of these amplifiers still use vacuum tubes and employ a thousand or more volts in the power supply circuit. The result of contacting this voltage is often fatal. **Always make certain the power cannot be energized when you are exposed to lethal voltages.** In case you forget this precaution, any equipment employing voltages greater than 50 volts should employ an **interlock**. This device, usually a power switch attached to the removable covers, automatically disables the power supply whenever entry is made into the cabinet. The covers also prevent radiation of RF energy. Sometimes it is necessary to troubleshoot a "hot box". If you **absolutely must** work on equipment which uses lethal voltages, always keep one hand in your pocket when the safety covers are off. (N4B03)(N4B07)

The Kenwood TS-850S, like other high frequency transceivers, generates more than 100 watts power output. This creates high RF voltages in the power amplifier stage that can cause an RF burn to the unfortunate service person who happens to contact it.

Fire!

The voltages used in most modern solid state transmitter/receivers will not cause electrical shock. The current available, however, can easily start a fire. As an example, if a paper clip should happen to short an unfused 12-volt, 40-ampere power supply, the metal clip would glow red-hot just like an automobile cigarette lighter. This can easily ignite combustible materials.

An Ounce of Prevention

Obviously you should not leave metal objects near your high amperage power supplies. Even with precautions, however, accidents can and do happen in the ham shack.

For a number of reasons, it is an excellent idea to install a key operated switch in the main power line of your Amateur station. If you have a mobile rig, disconnect the microphone and put it in the glove compartment when you are not using it. This will prevent your pesky kid brother or sister from tampering with your gear or creating an unsafe condition. (N4A01)(N4A02)(N4A03)

Stormy Weather

Lightning can cause havoc in your ham shack. It is not necessary for a "bolt" to strike your antenna in order to cause damage. Electrically charged clouds, passing overhead, can cause a buildup of electricity on antennas. The buildup, or charge, may eventually jump or discharge to ground. With proper grounding the charge will not accumulate on the antenna.

Even when lightning strikes hundreds of yards away, *an enormous electromagnetic field is generated.* This field will induce voltage in any metal objects within the field. Remember Hertz's spark experiments mentioned in Chapter One? Exactly the same thing can happen with your antenna. Very little voltage is required to damage the transistors in your radio equipment. In fact, it takes far less than the voltage required to create a spark.

If the lightning stroke is sufficiently strong, and your station is not adequately grounded, it can cause sparks to jump between your radio equipment. Even if the level is not lethal, it might be sufficient to burn out transistors or start a fire. A key operated power switch won't solve this problem.

You're Grounded!

It is not possible to stop the phenomena of lightning induced voltage and static electricity. We can, however, take steps to minimize the damage or harm caused by it. The first step is to properly ground all your radio equipment. The metal chassis of each piece of equipment should be connected together with a heavy copper wire. The gauge used for house wiring, #10 or #12 (available at most hardware stores), is quite adequate. This wire should run to ground by a short direct route. (N4A07)(N4A09)

In addition, you must ground the antenna and (if used) rotor or control wires with a switch (such as a knife switch) whenever there is a storm in the vicinity. Several companies sell grounding devices which can be left connected at all times. These are usually mounted outside the house. (N4A04)(N4A05)

This covers the situation when a storm comes up while you are away from home. If you don't install static discharge devices, it is a good idea to always ground the wires entering your station whenever you are not using your station. It's also a good idea to unplug your valuable equipment when it is not in use. (N4A06)

Where do you find a good ground connection? The preferred method is to install a ground rod in the earth just outside the window nearest the radio equipment. The ground rod should be at least 8 feet long and plated with copper, to be effective. These can be purchased at most Amateur Radio stores. They are driven into the ground with a sledge hammer. (N4A10)(N4A11)

Sometimes it is just not practical to install a ground rod. You may be on the upper story of an apartment building or your folks may object to your drilling holes in the wall of their tidy mortgaged bungalow. A "second best" ground is to connect to a cold water pipe. Why second best? Usually the plumber puts compound on the pipe joints. This may prevent a good electrical connection between pipes. (N4A08)

The MFJ AC voltmeter has an expanded scale for accurate measurement of AC line voltage.

Why a cold water pipe? The hot water pipes go to the water heater which is probably not grounded. In this case, static discharges are more likely to head for the electrical circuits or natural gas pipes instead of going directly to an earth ground. Even so, the static electricity will ultimately reach ground.

The National Electrical Code

House wiring would be a real "hodge-podge" if each electrician were allowed creative liberty in wiring the circuits. The National Electrical Code is a document which specifies construction practices, color codes and safety considerations. It even covers standard electrical safety rules when building an Amateur antenna. (T4A04)(T4A05)

There is another way that your radio equipment is grounded which should always be respected. Virtually all electronic equipment found in the hamshack uses a three-wire plug. Two lugs carry the power, while a round center pin is used for ground. This is where the green ground wire is connected. At the other end, the green wire is connected to the metal frame of a drill, electric saw or the metal chassis of an electronic product. **Never cut off this safety pin** or use an adapter that has no provision for grounding the green wire to the wall outlet. (T4A01)

This single-sideband linear power amplifier (the Ten-Tec "Titan") is rated at 1500 watts output.

While speaking of electrical wiring, we should mention the correct connection of the current carrying wires. Anything that breaks the electrical circuit (a fuse or switch) should be connected in series with the black (or red) wire of the power cord or house wiring. By the same token, the unswitched side of the wiring should use the white wire. In a mobile installation, the fuse always goes in series with the red wire connected to the source of 12 volts. (T4A02)(T4A03)(T4A06)

Maintaining these relationships is very important to minimize shock hazard in electronic equipment. Look at the two lugs that carry the current in the power cord. Did you ever notice they are a different size. This insures that you insert the plug correctly when there is no ground pin. This respect for polarity explains why the screws that secure the wiring on each side of a switch or light socket are a different color. (T4A07)

Electric Shock

Why all this concern about proper wiring? The answer is simple. **An electric current flowing through your body can kill you.** If you discover someone who is being burned by high voltage, you should turn off the power, call for emergency help and give CPR if needed (you do know how to apply CPR, don't you?). (T4A15)

Even voltages as low as 30 volts can be dangerous under certain conditions. However, it is not the voltage, but rather the current level that matters. Ever work on an automobile engine and get shocked by the ignition circuit? If so, it's likely that something in the order of 20,000 volts was conducted through your ole "bod." Fortunately, there was not enough conducted current to hurt you. (T4A11)

How does current affect you? Anything below five milliamperes (mA) is probably harmless. If the current increases to 50 mA, you will experience pain and muscular contractions that may prevent you from "letting go." Over *100 mA (one-tenth of an ampere)*, the heart will be affected and may cause death in people with heart problems or if the current is sustained. (T4A08)(T4A09)(T4A10)

For safety sake, **never wear jewelry** when working on equipment that has power applied to it. Make sure everyone in your family knows where the main power switch for your house or apartment is located, and how to shut off the electricity. Always place the power switch (either the master switch or transmitter high voltage power switch) where it is obvious to anyone and can be easily reached. Someone else may have to throw the switch if you can't let go! (T4A12)(T4A13)(T4A14)

RF Exposure

If you doubt that RF has the ability to cook things, ask for a demonstration of a microwave oven at your local discount store. Any concentration of radio frequency energy will raise the temperature of material in its' field. Microwave ovens operate near the Amateur 1270 MHz band. Ham equipment which operates in this range can cause heating effects from RF radiaiton. (N4B06)(T4D09)

Dish-shaped antennas, designed to work at micro wavelengths (above 1,000 MHz or 1 GigaHertz) concentrate RF energy so that it may be directed like a flashlight beam. If you happen to be standing at the focus point, you will quickly realize how that meatloaf feels in the microwave oven. You should never stand near any kind of antenna which concentrates RF energy (or open waveguide transmission line, for that matter) when the transmitter power is on. Always use a good quality of coaxial cable transmission line to minimize RF leakage. (N4B04)

Insofar as possible, your antenna (regardless of frequency or type) must be mounted high enough so that people cannot touch it. Even if the antenna is out of reach, you should *never transmit if someone is standing near it*. The strong field around an antenna can be very intense. (N4B02)(N4B10)

There is growing concern that the radiation from hand-held transceivers may be harmful if used constantly over long periods of time. There is no direct evidence to support this, but it is an excellent idea to keep the whip or "rubber duck" antenna on your hand-held *away from your head*. (N4B05)

Scientists at the American National Standards Institute (ANSI) have established maximum level standards for exposure from RF energy to the human body. These standards state the maximum safe RF exposure limits. (T4D11)(T4D12)

ANSI is concerned about the heating caused by RF energy. The standards in 30 to 300 MHz range are the most stringent since the human body absorbs RF energy the most in this range. The eyes are particularly sensitive to heating caused by this form of radiation. Always make sure to keep the antenna of a handheld transceiver *away from your eyes* when transmitting in this frequency range. (N4B01)(T4D10)(T4D13) (T4D14)

Hand-held units, which are operated near the head and eyes, should not have a power rating in excess of 7 watts according to ANSI. (T4D15)

Antenna Tuning and SWR

The last chapter mentioned that energy from the transmitter is fed through the transmission line to the antenna, where it is coupled to the environment. For this to occur, the antenna must be the **correct length** for the frequency in question. If it is too long or too short, it will lose efficiency as a coupling device. This can also happen if the electrical resistance (the impedance) of the antenna is incorrect (see *Chapter 9*).

In this case, what happens to the energy sent up to the antenna? Most of it will be radiated into space, but some will not. A portion of the energy will be *reflected* back down the transmission line to the transmitter. The antenna can't absorb all the energy and sends some back to the transmitter. The transmitter doesn't want it either—it just got rid of it, and back up the transmission line it goes.

The reflected energy, passed back and forth like a hot potato, is called **standing waves**. The intensity of these waves is measured with a device called an **SWR meter**. An SWR meter can also be used to indicate the **impedance matching** condition between the transmitter and the antenna. A reading of 1:1 indicates a *perfect condition*, while anything above 2:1 is an *unacceptable match* which can damage your transmitter. Anything in between would indicate a *fairly good impedance match*. The SWR meter can also indicate an open or shorted transmission line if the SWR reading is exceptionally high. A poor or intermittent electrical connection in the antenna might be indicated by an erratic or jumpy meter reading. (N4C01)(N4C02)(N4C03) (N4C04)(N4C05)(N4C06)(N4C07)(N4C08)

As mentioned, the antenna must be the correct length to be most efficient at a specific frequency. If the antenna is too *long* it will tune *lower* than the desired frequency. If the antenna is too *short*, it will tune *above* the desired frequency. The SWR meter can be used to indicate the frequency to which the antenna is tuned. Let's say, for example, you measure an SWR of 2.5:1 at the low end of the Amateur band and 5:1 at the high end. Both numbers are excessively high but improving at the low end. Just like a golf score, 2.5 is better than 5 so the SWR is improving at the low frequency. This means that the antenna is probably tuned below the low end of the band. Remember that "long is low" so the antenna is probably too long for the band in question. (N4C09)(N4C10)

If you are adjusting an antenna for lowest SWR, the meter should be connected right **at the antenna terminals** for best accuracy. This is because a long transmission line can mask poor SWR readings.

One occasionally hears the standing wave radio meter called an SWR bridge or **reflectometer**. The reflectometer or SWR meter is used to

The MFJ SWR meter has a dual-meter scale which shows the forward and reverse energy at the same time.

The MFJ Antenna Bridge can be used to measure not only SWR, but the impedance of an antenna system.

measure impedance mismatch in an antenna system. It is connected between the 50 ohm impedance transmitter output and the transmission line to the antenna. If the antenna system (including transmission line) also measures 50 ohms impedance, there will be no reflected power. The SWR meter will indicate a perfect 1:1 impedance match. If the reading is higher than 1:1, it indicates an impedance mismatch. On some SWR meters, an adjustment and calibrated scale will tell the user the impedance of the antenna. (T4B08)(T4C08) (T4C09)

The transmitter antenna jack is also where a power output measuring device should be connected for best accuracy. (T4B07)

A simple SWR meter measures the **relative** power delivered to, and reflected by, the antenna system. More elegant versions are called directional watt-meters and are calibrated in watts forward and watts reflected. (T4B09)

The only time the forward power reading will be accurate is when there is no reflected power. The reflected power will artificially add to the forward power reading and the forward reading will by higher than the actual level. For example, let's say a transmitter that produces 80 watts is connected to an antenna that shows 10 watts reflected power on the directional watt-meter. In this circumstance, the forward power will actually read 90 watts, 10 watts more than the transmitter is capable of producing. If a transmitter shows 96 watts forward and 4 watts reflected, the transmitter is actually producing 92 watts. (T4B10)(TT4B11)

You should always use an SWR meter or wattmeter that is calibrated for the frequency in use. *Bird Wattmeters*, for example have replacable "slugs" or inserts for different power levels and frequency ranges. If you use an insert designed to measure power between 3 and 30 MHz, it may not be accurate at all when measuring UHF power. (N4C11)(T4C10)(T4C11)

Most modern (meaning all solid-state) transmitters and transceivers (a combination transmitter-receiver) employ a circuit to protect the power amplifier transistors, which supply the output power, against excessive SWR. Without protection, excessive SWR can cause high RF voltages to exceed the breakdown rating of these transistors. In a protected transmitter, the transmitter will shut down and provide little or no power output when the SWR value rises above a certain point. This can be somewhat inconvenient when you are trying to tune an antenna system. But it is even more annoying (and expensive!) to take your rig to the repair shop to have the power amplifier transistors replaced!

This is the Amateur TV station of Dave, WB0ZJP. Note the quantity of homebrew equipment.

What Happened To My Picture?

As more and more people become radio Amateurs, interference due to close proximity of an Amateur station becomes more common. The energy from a nearby transmitter can be so strong where you live, that it might completely paralyze your ham radio receiver. Technically this is called receiver **overload**. (N4D01)

A typical Amateur receiver is designed to "hear" signals in the order of a millionth of a volt (a microvolt). The signal from another ham down the street could induce several volts in the antenna connected to your receiver. This would certainly overload the receiver, no matter how much you paid for it. An indication of **receiver overload** is reception of the local Amateur all over the dial, independent of frequency, no matter where you tune. (N4D02)

Another manifestation of receiver overload is interference by your transmitter with nearby television receivers. The signal radiated by your antenna can also induce several volts of energy in a nearby TV antenna. If the TV set connected to this antenna is not designed to reject the interference, your signal can "chop up" the picture on all channels. If this occurs no matter where you are transmitting, it is almost certainly due to overload of the television receiver. (N4D03)

How do you design a TV set to reject this sort of interference? By incorporating a simple device which passes the high frequency television signals but rejects your low frequency transmitter signals. The device is called a **high pass filter** and is discussed in *Chapter 7 (Filters)*. (N4D05)

Some TV manufacturers do not include high pass filters in order to reduce costs. A high pass filter can be added to eliminate this sort of interference. This is done right at the antenna terminals of the television set.

The FSTY-430 fastscan TV transmitter from AEA produces a signal that duplicates that of a commercial TV station.

If your transmitter (operating on 15 meters, for example) bothers TV reception only on specific channels (usually the lower two or three), it indicates that your rig is emitting *spurious signals*. The most common spurious is called a **harmonic**. Harmonics can cause interference to other services and can result in out-of-band transmissions. (N4D04)

A harmonic is a **mathematical multiple** of the transmitting frequency. For example, if you operate on the 28 MHz band, your second harmonic at 56 MHz is very close to Channel 2 (56-60 MHz). Other harmonics might interfere with commercial frequencies rather than a television channel. Unwanted harmonics can be accentuated if a poorly tuned transmitter is feeding a multiband antenna. (N4D07)(N4D08)

A high pass filter on the TV set will not solve this problem. The spurious signal from your transmitter is near the desired television channel or station so there is no way to filter it out at the receiver. In this instance you must add a filter between your transmitter and the transmission line. This harmonic filter is called **a low pass filter**. It allows the low frequencies you are transmitting to pass through, but suppresses the high frequency harmonics that interfere with other services. (N4D06)

An improperly tuned transmitter or poorly matched antenna (or a multi-band antenna) can increase the problem of harmonic radiation. It is a good idea to incorporate a low pass filter in your transmission line, even if you do not hear reports of television interference by your station. Poor shielding in a transmitter or power amplifier can allow unwanted signals (such as harmonics) to "escape" from the box. If you work on a power amplifier, always be certain that all shields are replaced, exactly as you found them, before turning the amplifier on. (N4D09)(N4D10) (T4D16)

If you are notified that your station is interfering with someones' TV reception, what should you do? First, be responsive and friendly. Check your own television set to see if you also have interference. If your set is bothered also, it probably means that your transmitter is putting out some "garbage" and you should add a low pass filter. (N4D11)

If your set is "clean", it means that your neighbor's television is not well equipped to reject Amateur Radio interference. In almost every case a simple high pass filter (available from an Amateur Radio store) will solve the problem.

Test Equipment

The most important devices an Amateur can own are used to make measurements. The SWR meter mentioned earlier is probably the most useful. Let's discuss some of the other types of Amateur *test equipment*.

Marker Generators—Equipment that produce test signals are quite useful in the ham radio "shack." For example a **marker generator** places an accurate, stable, crystal controlled marker (a tone or whistle) at various intervals on the receiver dial. In the last chapter, we learned that the frequencies between 50.0 and 50.1 MHz are reserved for CW operation. A 100 kHz (0.1 MHz) marker generator would cause a tone to be heard each 100 kHz. Thus, you would hear the marker at 50.0 and 50.1 MHz. This can be used to warn you of the CW band edges. Naturally, you can switch off the marker generator once you have noted where the limits are. A marker generator is sometimes called a **crystal calibrator** since it can be used to accurately calibrate the receiver dial. (T4C01)(T4C02)(T4C03)

You can calibrate the calibrator by tuning your receiver to one of the frequencies where National Bureau of Standards stations WWV (Colorado) and WWVH (Hawaii) transmit time and frequency standard signals. The most popular frequencies are 5.0, 10.0 and 15.0 MHz. You can also check the relative calibration of your receiver by seeing how closely your dial reads to these frequencies when you tune them in. (T4C04)(T4C05)

Signal Generators—A similar device, but variable in frequency, is called an **RF signal generator**. This device produces a stable, low level variable signal that can be set to a desired frequency. Signal generators are used for receiver testing and checking alignment. (T4C06)(T4C07)

The Multimeter—One of the most useful pieces of test equipment found in the ham shack is called a **multimeter** or V-O-M (volt-ohm-milliampere) meter. As the name implies, it will measure electromotive force (voltage), resistance (ohms) and current (amperes). (T4B06)

The multimeter has a switch on the front panel to select the function and range. To measure voltage, the test leads are placed across or in parallel with the source. To measure current (amperes or milliamperes), the meter leads are connected in series with the source of current. (T4B01)(T4B04)

The switch changes the range of the multimeter by connecting resistors to the meter. To increase the range of a *voltmeter*, resistors would be *connected in series* with the meter movement. Thus it would be possible to read 0-1, 0-10 and 0-100 volts with the same zero-to-ten meter scale. (T4B02)(T4B03)

Gordon West, WB6NOA, demonstrates the use of Amateur Radio test equipment at his radio school in Southern California.

To increase the range of an *ammeter*, resistors would be *connected in parallel* with the meter movement. Again, the same zero to ten meter scale calibration could be used to read 0-100 mA, 0-1 ampere and 0-10 amperes, and so on. (T4B05)

Dummy Antenna—The **dummy antenna** is also called a **dummy load**, and should be found in every hamshack. It is used for off-the-air transmitter testing and tuning. (T4D01)

The dummy antenna is connected in place of the antenna transmission line. It tricks the transmitter into thinking it is connected to a perfect antenna. The dummy load does not radiate any signal or cause interference to other stations. (T4D02)(T4D04) (T4D05)

The main component of the device is a *large carbon composition resistor* (see *Chapter 6*). Resistors made with resistance wire (such as sometimes seen on old-fashioned electric stoves) are never used. The wire will have inductance which can confuse the SWR meter. Sometimes the resistor is immersed in a container of mineral oil. This will keep the dummy load cool while it absorbs transmitter power. The cooling increases the power rating of the dummy load for a given resistor size. (T4D03)(T4D07)

The power rating should be observed to avoid damaging the resistive element. Always use a dummy antenna load which matches the power rating of the transmitter to which it is connected. (T4D06)

S-Meter—While this is not a separate instrument, it is useful as a piece of "test equipment" for measuring strength of signals. The **S-meter** is included in most Amateur receivers to indicate relative signal strength (see *Chapter 2- Am I Getting Out?*). (T4D08)

Now it's time to see if you absorbed all this knowledge. Here are the questions from the Novice and Technician pools.

Novice Subelement 4 (4 questions)

N4A01—How could you best keep unauthorized persons from using your Amateur station at home? (A) Use a carrier-operated relay in the main power line; (B) Use a key-operated on/off switch in the main power line; (C) Put a "Danger - High Voltage" sign in the station; (D) Put fuses in the main power line.

N4A02—How could you best keep unauthorized persons from using a mobile Amateur station in your car? (A) Disconnect the microphone when you are not using it; (B) Put a "do not touch" sign on the radio; (C) Turn the radio off when you are not using it; (D) Tune the radio to an unused frequency when you are done using it.

N4A03—Why would you use a key-operated on/off switch in the main power line of your station? (A) To keep unauthorized persons from using your station; (B) For safety, in case the main fuses fail; (C) To keep the power company from turning off your electricity during an emergency; (D) For safety, to turn off the station in the event of an emergency.

N4A04—Why should you ground all antenna and rotator cables when your Amateur station is not in use? (A) To lock the antenna system in one position; (B) To avoid radio frequency interference; (C) To save electricity; (D) To protect the station and building from lightning damage.

N4A05—How can an antenna system best be protected from lightning damage? (A) Install a balun at the antenna feed point; (B) Install an RF choke in the antenna feed line; (C) Ground all antennas when they are not in use; (D) Install a fuse in the antenna feed line.

N4A06—How can Amateur station equipment best be protected from lightning damage? (A) Use heavy insulation on the wiring; (B) Never turn off the equipment; (C) Disconnect the ground system from all radios; (D) Disconnect all equipment from the power lines and antenna cables.

N4A07—For best protection from electrical shock, what should be grounded in an Amateur station? (A) The power supply primary; (B) All station equipment; (C) The antenna feed line; (D) The AC power mains.

N4A08—What is usually a good indoor grounding point for an Amateur station? (A) A metallic cold water pipe; (B) A plastic cold water pipe; (C) A window screen; (D) A metallic natural gas pipe.

N4A09—Where should you connect the chassis of each piece of your station equipment to best protect against electrical shock? (A) To insulated shock mounts; (B) To the antenna; (C) To a good ground connection; (D) To a circuit breaker.

N4A10—Which of these materials is best for a ground rod driven into the earth? (A) Hard plastic; (B) Copper or copper-clad steel; (C) Iron or steel; (D) Fiberglass.

N4A11—If you ground your station equipment to a ground rod driven into the earth, what is the shortest length the rod should be? (A) 4 feet; (B) 6 feet; (C) 8 feet; (D) 10 feet.

N4B01—What should you do for safety when operating at 1270 MHz? (A) Make sure that an RF leakage filter is installed at the antenna feed point; (B) Keep antenna away from your eyes when RF is applied; (C) Make sure the standing wave ratio is low before you conduct a test; (D) Never use a shielded horizontally polarized antenna.

N4B02—What should you do for safety if you put up a UHF transmitting antenna? (A) Make sure the antenna will be in a place where no one can get near it when you are transmitting; (B) Make sure that RF field screens are in place; (C) Make sure the antenna is near the ground to keep its RF energy pointing in the correct direction; (D) Make sure you connect an RF leakage filter at the antenna feed point.

N4B03—What should you do for safety before removing the shielding on a UHF power amplifier? (A) Make sure all RF screens are in place at the antenna feed line; (B) Make sure the antenna feed line is properly grounded; (C) Make sure the amplifier cannot accidentally be turned on; (D) Make sure that RF leakage filters are connected.

N4B04—Why should you use only good quality coaxial cable and connectors for a UHF antenna system? (A) To keep RF loss low; (B) To keep television interference high; (C) To keep the power going to your antenna system from getting too high; (D) To keep the standing wave ratio of your antenna system high.

N4B05—Why should you make sure the antenna of a hand held transceiver is not close to your head when transmitting? (A) To help the antenna radiate energy equally in all directions; (B) To reduce your exposure the radio-frequency energy; (C) To use your body to reflect the signal in one direction; (D) To keep static charges from building up.

N4B06—Microwave oven radiation is similar to what type of Amateur station RF radiation? (A) Signals in the 3.5 MHz range; (B) Signals in the 21 MHz range; (C) Signals in the 50 MHz range; (D) Signals in the 1270 MHz range.

N4B07—Why would there be a switch in a high-voltage power supply to turn off the power if its cabinet is opened? (A) To keep dangerous RF radiation from leaking out through an open cabinet; (B) To keep dangerous RF radiation from coming in through an open cabinet; (C) To turn the power supply off when it is not being used; (D) To keep anyone opening the cabinet from getting shocked by dangerous high voltages.

N4B08—What kind of safety equipment should you wear if you are working on an antenna tower? (A) A grounding chain; (B) A reflective vest of approved color; (C) A flashing red, yellow or white light; (D) A carefully inspected safety belt, hard hat and safety glasses.

N4B09—Why should you wear a safety belt if you are working on an antenna tower? (A) To safely hold your tools so they don't fall and injure someone on the ground; (B) To keep the tower from becoming unbalanced while you are working; (C) To safely bring any tools you might use up and down the tower; (D) To prevent you from accidentally falling.

N4B10—For safety, how high should you place a horizontal wire antenna? (A) High enough so that no one can touch any part of it from the ground; (B) As close to the ground as possible; (C) Just high enough so you can easily reach it for adjustments or repairs; (D) Above high-voltage electrical lines.

N4B11—Why should you wear a hard hat if you are on the ground helping someone work on an antenna tower? (A) So you won't be hurt if the tower should accidentally fall; (B) To keep RF energy away from your head during antenna testing; (C) To protect your head from something dropped from the tower; (D) So someone passing by will know that work is being done on the tower and will stay away.

N4C01—What instrument is used to measure standing wave ratio? (A) An ohmmeter; (B) An ammeter; (C) An SWR meter; (D) A current bridge.

N4C02—What instrument is used to measure the relative impedance match between an antenna and its feed line? (A) An ammeter; (B) An ohmmeter; (C) A voltmeter; (D) An SWR meter.

N4C03—Where would you connect an SWR meter to measure standing wave ratio? (A) Between the feed line and the antenna; (B) Between the transmitter and the power supply; (C) Between the transmitter and the receiver; (D) Between the transmitter and the ground.

N4C04—What does an SWR reading of 1:1 mean? (A) An antenna for another frequency band is probably connected; (B) The best impedance match has been attained; (C) No power is going to the antenna; (D) The SWR meter is broken.

N4C05—What does an SWR reading of less than 1.5:1 mean? (A) An impedance match which is too low; (B) An impedance mismatch; something may be wrong with the antenna system; (C) A fairly good impedance match; (D) An antenna gain of 1.5.

N4C06—What does an SWR reading of 4:1 mean? (A) An impedance match which is too low; (B) An impedance match which is good, but not the best; (C) An antenna gain of 4; (D) An impedance mismatch; something may be wrong with the antenna system.

N4C07—What kind of SWR reading may mean poor electrical contact between parts of an antenna system? (A) A jumpy reading; (B) A very low reading; (C) No reading at all; (D) A negative reading.

N4C08—What does a very high SWR reading mean? (A) The antenna is the wrong length, or there may be an open or shorted connection somewhere in the feed line; (B) The signals coming from the antenna are unusually strong, which means very good radio conditions; (C) The transmitter is putting out more power than normal, showing that it is about to go bad; (D) There is a large amount of solar radiation, which means very poor radio conditions.

N4C09—If an SWR reading at the low frequency end of an Amateur band is 2.5:1, and is 5:1 at the high frequency end of the same band, what does this tell you about your 1/2-wavelength dipole antenna? (A) The antenna is broadbanded; (B) The antenna is too long for operation on the band; (C) The antenna is too short for operation on the band; (D) The antenna is just right for operation on the band.

N4C10—If an SWR reading at the low frequency end of an Amateur band is 5:1, and 2.5:1 at the high frequency end of the same band, what does this tell you about your 1/2-wavelength dipole antenna? (A) The antenna is broadbanded; (B) The antenna is too long for operation on the band; (C) The antenna is too short for operation on the band; (D) The antenna is just right for operation on the band.

N4C11—If you use a 3-30 MHz RF-power meter at UHF frequencies, how accurate will its readings be? (A) They may not be accurate at all; (B) They will be accurate enough to get by; (C) They will be accurate but the readings must be divided by two; (D) They will be accurate but the readings must be multiplied by two.

N4D01—What is meant by receiver overload? (A) Too much voltage from the power supply; (B) Too much current from the power supply; (C) Interference caused by strong signals from a nearby transmitter; (D) Interference caused by turning the volume up too high.

N4D02—What is one way to tell if radio-frequency interference to a receiver is caused by front-end overload? (A) If connecting a low-pass filter to the transmitter greatly cuts down the interference; (B) If the interference is about the same no matter what frequency is used for the transmitter; (C) If connecting a low-pass filter to the receiver greatly cuts down the interference; (D) If grounding the receiver makes the problem worse.

N4D03—If your neighbor reports television interference whenever you are transmitting from your Amateur station, no matter what frequency band you use, what is probably the cause of the interference? (A) Too little transmitter harmonic suppression; (B) Receiver VR tube discharge; (C) Receiver overload; (D) Incorrect antenna length.

N4D04—If your neighbor reports television interference on one or two channels only when you are transmitting on the 15-meter band, what is probably the cause of the interference? (A) Too much low-pass filtering on the transmitter; (B) De-ionization of the ionosphere near your neighbor's TV antenna; (C) TV receiver front-end overload; (D) Harmonic radiation from your transmitter.

N4D05—What type of filter should be connected to a TV receiver as the first step in trying to prevent RF overload from an Amateur HF station transmission? (A) Low-pass; (B) High-pass; (C) Band pass; (D) Notch.

N4D06—What type of filter might be connected to an Amateur HF transmitter to cut down on harmonic radiation? (A) A key-click filter; (B) A low-pass filter; (C) A high-pass filter; (D) A CW filter.

N4D07—What is meant by harmonic radiation? (A) Unwanted signals at frequencies which are multiples of the fundamental (chosen) frequency; (B) Unwanted signals that are combined with a 60-Hz hum; (C) Unwanted signals caused by sympathetic vibrations from a nearby transmitter; (D) Signals which cause skip propagation to occur.

N4D08—Why is harmonic radiation from an Amateur station not wanted? (A) It may cause interference to other stations and may result in out-of-band signals; (B) It uses large amounts of electric power; (C) It may cause sympathetic vibrations in nearby transmitters; (D) It may cause auroras in the air.

N4D09—What type of interference may come from a multi-band antenna connected to a poorly tuned transmitter? (A) Harmonic radiation; (B) Auroral distortion; (C) Parasitic excitation; (D) Intermodulation.

N4D10—What is the main purpose of shielding in a transmitter? (A) It gives the low-pass filter a solid support; (B) It helps the sound quality of transmitters; (C) It prevents unwanted RF radiation; (D) It helps keep electronic parts warmer and more stable.

N4D11—If you are told that your Amateur station is causing television interference, what should you do? (A) First make sure that your station is operating properly, and that it does not cause interference to your own television; (B) Immediately turn off your transmitter and contact the nearest FCC office for assistance; (C) Connect a high-pass filter to the transmitter output and a low-pass filter to the antenna-input terminals of the television; (D) Continue operating normally, because you have no reason to worry about the interference

Technician Subelement 4 (4 questions)

T4A01—Where should the green wire in a three-wire AC line cord be connected in a power supply? (A) To the fuse; (B) To the "hot" side of the power switch; (C) To the chassis; (D) To the white wire.

T4A02—Where should the black (or red) wire in a three-wire AC line cord be connected in a power supply? (A) To the white wire; (B) To the green wire; (C) To the chassis; (D) To the fuse.

T4A03—Where should the white wire in a three-wire AC line cord be connected in a power supply? (A) To the side of the power transformer's primary winding that has a fuse; (B) To the side of the power transformer's primary winding that does not have a fuse; (C) To the chassis; (D) To the black wire.

T4A04—What document is used by almost every US city as the basis for electrical safety requirements for power wiring and antennas? (A) The Code of Federal Regulations; (B) The Proceedings of the IEEE; (C) The ITU Radio Regulations; (D) The National Electrical Code.

T4A05—What document would you use to see if you comply with standard electrical safety rules when building an Amateur antenna? (A) The Code of Federal Regulations; (B) The Proceedings of the IEEE; (C) The National Electrical Code; (D) The ITU Radio Regulations.

T4A06—Where should fuses be connected on a mobile transceiver's DC power cable? (A) Between the red and black wires; (B) In series with just the black wire; (C) In series with just the red wire; (D) In series with both the red and black wires.

T4A07—Why is the retaining screw in one terminal of a wall outlet made of brass while the other one is silver colored? (A) To prevent corrosion; (B) To indicate correct wiring polarity; (C) To better conduct current; (D) To reduce skin effect.

T4A08—How much electrical current flowing through the human body is usually fatal? (A) As little as 1/10 of an ampere; (B) Approximately 10 amperes; (C) More than 20 amperes; (D) Current flow through the human body is never fatal.

T4A09—Which body organ can be fatally affected by a very small amount of electrical current? (A) The heart; (B) The brain; (C) The liver; (D) The lungs.

T4A10—How much electrical current flowing through the human body is usually painful? (A) As little as 1/500 of an ampere; (B) Approximately 10 amperes; (C) More than 20 amperes; (D) Current flow through the human body is never painful.

T4A11—What is the minimum voltage which is usually dangerous to humans? (A) 30 volts; (B) 100 volts; (C) 1000 volts; (D) 2000 volts.

T4A12—Where should the main power switch for a high-voltage power supply be located? (A) Inside the cabinet, to kill the power if the cabinet is opened; (B) On the back side of the cabinet, out of sight; (C) Anywhere that can be seen and reached easily; (D) A high voltage power supply should not be switch-operated.

T4A13—What precaution should you take when leaning over a power amplifier? (A) Take your shoes off; (B) Watch out for loose jewelry contacting high voltage; (C)

Shield your face from the heat produced by the power supply; (D) Watch out for sharp edges which may snag your clothing.

T4A14—What is an important safety rule concerning the main electrical box in your home? (A) Make sure the door cannot be opened easily; (B) Make sure something is placed in front of the door so no one will be able to get to it easily; (C) Make sure others in your home know where it is and how to shut off the electricity; (D) Warn others in your home never to touch the switches, even in an emergency.

T4A15—What should you do if you discover someone who is being burned by high voltage? (A) Run from the area so you won't be burned too; (B) Turn off the power, call for emergency help and give CPR if needed; (C) Immediately drag the person away from the high voltage; (D) Wait for a few minutes to see if the person can get away from the high voltage on their own, then try to help.

T4B01—How is a voltmeter usually connected to a circuit under test? (A) In series with the circuit; (B) In parallel with the circuit; (C) In quadrature with the circuit; (D) In phase with the circuit.

T4B02—How can the range of a voltmeter be increased? (A) By adding resistance in series with the circuit under test; (B) By adding resistance in parallel with the circuit under test; (C) By adding resistance in series with the meter, between the meter and the circuit under test ; (D) By adding resistance in parallel with the meter, between the meter and the circuit under test.

T4B03—What happens inside a voltmeter when you switch it from a lower to a higher voltage range? (A) Resistance is added in series with the meter; (B) Resistance is added in parallel with the meter; (C) Resistance is reduced in series with the meter; (D) Resistance is reduced in parallel with the meter.

T4B04—How is an ammeter usually connected to a circuit under test? (A) In series with the circuit; (B) In parallel with the circuit; (C) In quadrature with the circuit; (D) In phase with the circuit.

T4B05—How can the range of an ammeter be increased? (A) By adding resistance in series with the circuit under test; (B) By adding resistance in parallel with the circuit under test; (C) By adding resistance in series with the meter; (D) By adding resistance in parallel with the meter.

T4B06—What does a multimeter measure? (A) SWR and power; (B) Resistance, capacitance and inductance; (C) Resistance and reactance; (D) Voltage, current and resistance.

T4B07—Where should an RF wattmeter be connected for the most accurate readings of transmitter output power? (A) At the transmitter output connector; (B) At the antenna feed point; (C) One-half wavelength from the transmitter output; (D) One-half wavelength from the antenna feed point.

T4B08—At what line impedance do most RF wattmeters usually operate? (A) 25 ohms; (B) 50 ohms; (C) 100 ohms; (D) 300 ohms.

T4B09—What does a directional wattmeter measure? (A) Forward and reflected power; (B) The directional pattern of an antenna; (C) The energy used by a transmitter; (D) Thermal heating in a load resistor.

T4B10—If a directional RF wattmeter reads 90 watts forward power and 10 watts reflected power, what is the actual transmitter output power? (A) 10 watts; (B) 80 watts; (C) 90 watts; (D) 100 watts.

T4B11—If a directional RF wattmeter reads 96 watts forward power and 4 watts reflected power, what is the actual transmitter output power? (A) 80 watts; (B) 88 watts; (C) 92 watts; (D) 100 watts.

T4C01—What is a marker generator? (A) A high-stability oscillator that generates reference signals at exact frequency intervals; (B) A low-stability oscillator that "sweeps" through a range of frequencies; (C) A low-stability oscillator used to inject a signal into a circuit under test; (D) A high-stability oscillator which can produce a wide range of frequencies and amplitudes.

T4C02—How is a marker generator used? (A) To calibrate the tuning dial on a receiver; (B) To calibrate the volume control on a receiver; (C) To test the amplitude linearity of a transmitter; (D) To test the frequency deviation of a transmitter.

T4C03—What device is used to inject a frequency calibration signal into a receiver? (A) A calibrated voltmeter; (B) A calibrated oscilloscope; (C) A calibrated wavemeter; (D) A crystal calibrator.

T4C04—What frequency standard may be used to calibrate the tuning dial of a receiver? (A) A calibrated voltmeter; (B) Signals from WWV and WWVH; (C) A deviation meter; (D) A sweep generator.

T4C05—How might you check the accuracy of your receiver's tuning dial? (A) Tune to the frequency of a shortwave broadcasting station; (B) Tune to a popular Amateur net frequency; (C) Tune to one of the frequencies of station WWV or WWVH; (D) Tune to another Amateur station and ask what frequency the operator is using.

T4C06—What device produces a stable, low-level signal that can be set to a desired frequency? (A) A wavemeter; (B) A reflectometer; (C) A signal generator; (D) An oscilloscope.

T4C07—What is an RF signal generator used for? (A) Measuring RF signal amplitudes; (B) Aligning tuned circuits; (C) Adjusting transmitter impedance-matching networks; (D) Measuring transmission line impedances.

T4C08—What device can measure an impedance mismatch in your antenna system? (A) A field-strength meter; (B) An ammeter; (C) A wavemeter; (D) A reflectometer.

T4C09—Where should a reflectometer be connected for best accuracy when reading the impedance match between an antenna and its feed line? (A) At the antenna feed point; (B) At the transmitter output connector; (C) At the midpoint of the feed line; (D) Anywhere along the feed line.

T4C10—If you use a 3-30 MHz RF power meter for VHF, how accurate will its readings be? (A) They will not be accurate; (B) They will be accurate enough to get by; (C) If it properly calibrates to full scale in the set position, they may be accurate; (D) They will be accurate providing the readings are multiplied by 4.5.

T4C11—If you use a 3-30 MHz SWR meter for VHF, how accurate will its readings be? (A) They will not be accurate; (B) They will be accurate enough to get by; (C) If it properly calibrates to full scale in the set position, they may be accurate; (D) They will be accurate providing the readings are multiplied by 4.5.

T4D01—What device should be connected to a transmitter's output when you are making transmitter adjustments? (A) A multimeter; (B) A reflectometer; (C) A receiver; (D) A dummy antenna.

T4D02—What is a dummy antenna? (A) An nondirectional transmitting antenna; (B) A nonradiating load for a transmitter; (C) An antenna used as a reference for gain measurements; (D) A flexible antenna usually used on hand held transceivers.

T4D03—What is the main component of a dummy antenna? (A) A wire-wound resistor; (B) An iron-core coil; (C) A noninductive resistor; (D) An air-core coil.

T4D04—What device is used in place of an antenna during transmitter tests so that no signal is radiated? (A) An antenna matcher; (B) A dummy antenna; (C) A low-pass filter; (D) A decoupling resistor.

T4D05—Why would you use a dummy antenna? (A) For off-the-air transmitter testing; (B) To reduce output power; (C) To give comparative signal reports; (D) To allow antenna tuning without causing interference.

T4D06—What minimum rating should a dummy antenna have for use with a 100-watt single-sideband phone transmitter? (A) 100 watts continuous; (B) 141 watts continuous; (C) 175 watts continuous; (D) 200 watts continuous.

T4D07—Why might a dummy antenna get warm when in use? (A) Because it stores electric current; (B) Because it stores radio waves; (C) Because it absorbs static electricity; (D) Because it changes RF energy into heat.

T4D08—What is used to measure relative signal strength in a receiver? (A) An S meter; (B) An RST meter; (C) A signal deviation meter; (D) An SSB meter.

T4D09—How can exposure to a large amount of RF energy affect body tissue? (A) It causes radiation poisoning; (B) It heats the tissue; (C) It paralyzes the tissue; (D) It produces genetic changes in the tissue.

T4D10—Which body organ is the most likely to be damaged from the heating effects of RF radiation? (A) Eyes; (B) Hands; (C) Heart; (D) Liver.

T4D11—What organization has published safety guidelines for the maximum limits of RF energy near the human body? (A) The Institute of Electrical and Electronics Engineers (IEEE); (B) The Federal Communications Commission (FCC); (C) The Environmental Protection Agency (EPA); (D) The American National Standards Institute (ANSI).

T4D12—What is the purpose of the ANSI RF protection guide? (A) It lists all RF frequency allocations for interference protection; (B) It gives RF exposure limits for the human body; (C) It sets transmitter power limits for interference protection; (D) It sets antenna height limits for aircraft protection.

T4D13—According to the ANSI RF protection guide, what frequencies cause us the greatest risk from RF energy? (A) 3 to 30 MHz; (B) 300 to 3000 MHz; (C) Above 1500 MHz; (D) 30 to 300 MHz.

T4D14—Why is the limit of exposure to RF the lowest in the frequency range of 30 MHz to 300 MHz, according to the ANSI RF protection guide? (A) There are more transmitters operating in this range; (B) There are fewer transmitters operating in this range; (C) Most transmissions in this range are for a longer time; (D) The human body absorbs RF energy the most in this range.

T4D15—According to the ANSI RF protection guide, what is the maximum safe power output to the antenna of a hand held VHF or UHF radio? (A) 125 milliwatts; (B) 7 watts; (C) 10 watts; (D) 25 watts.

T4D16—After you have opened a VHF power amplifier to make internal tuning adjustments, what should you do before you turn the amplifier on? (A) Remove all amplifier shielding to ensure maximum cooling; (B) Make sure that the power interlock switch is bypassed so you can test the amplifier; (C) Be certain all amplifier shielding is fastened in place; (D) Be certain no antenna is attached so that you will not cause any interference.

Chapter

Electrical Principles

After you finish this Chapter, you're halfway through the test preparation! You will be asked four questions from the Novice test (2) and two questions from the Technician question pool (3A) related to Electrical Principles. There are no questions in the test related to "The World of The Atom." However, this chapter can provide you with a comprehensive understanding of electronics if you care to study it. The principles described in this first section provide the underlying foundation of electronics. You should, at a minimum, study and understand the paragraphs which end in question numbers in parenthesis.

The World of The Atom

The entire science of electronics is based on the behavior of that minute particle, the **electron.** To understand the electron, what it does and why it does it, we have to observe the electron in its home territory, the world of the **atom.**

The atom is constructed somewhat like our own solar system. It has a central sun (the **nucleus**) and a number of planets (the electrons) revolving or orbiting around it. The nucleus, or core, is comprised of a number of positively charged particles called **protons.**

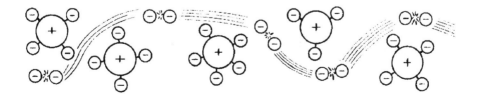

Similarly, the planets revolving around the nucleus are called electrons. They are tiny particles of negative electricity. It should be understood that this explanation is somewhat simplified. Sometimes there are electrons in the nucleus. There are also some other minor types of particles within the atom. However, we are primarily interested in the electrons.

All matter is basically composed of electrons and protons, each carrying an **electric charge**. The difference in characteristics of various substances is dependent on the number and position of the protons and electrons which make up each atom. This is true whether the substance is gold, silver, glass or Coca Cola.

Electrons tend to repel each other with relatively enormous force. Protons react against other protons in the same way. But electrons have a strong attraction for protons, and protons feel the same way about electrons.

This characteristic provides us with one of the basic laws of electricity: *Like charges repel and unlike charges attract.* If this were not so, atoms and molecules would be flying apart in all directions. It is only the attractive force between the positive charge of the nucleus and the negative charge of the planetary electrons which holds them together.

This delicate balance between charges within the atom or molecule may be upset, however. The substance may lose a few electrons from the outermost orbit, or this same orbit may be constantly seeking to add a few more electrons.

If either of these two events occur, the body itself is said to be **charged**. As an example, consider the old trick of running a comb briskly through the hair and then using it to pick up bits of paper by static attraction. In this case, friction has caused the comb to gain of lose some electrons and become charged.

If the comb has lost electrons, the negative charges in the orbit no longer cancel the positive ones in the nucleus, and the substance is said to be positively charged. If the comb has added electrons, their force now exceeds that in each nucleus, and the substance is negatively charged. This leads us to another fundamental electronic law: *A negative charge indicates an excess of electrons, while a positive charge results from an electron deficiency.*

The reader should understand that we cannot really "make" electricity. We can cause electrons to move from place to place. But whether we use friction to create the movement, or a dynamo or a solar battery, we are simply controlling electrons which are already there. A battery or generator does not create electricity any more than a pump creates water.

The SG-2000 is both a ham and commercial transceiver, FCC type accepted for marine and aeronautical service.

Let's get back to our hair and comb experiment. The charge developed between the two bodies can be easily discharged. Simply touch the comb to the hair without the friction which caused the charge and the charge disappears. But note that the bodies themselves do not actually have to touch to cause a discharge.

Suppose instead that one end of a copper wire touches the hair and the comb is touched to the other end of the wire. Now when we try to pick up the bits of paper with the comb, nothing happens. The charge has been equalized or discharged. But how? Obviously electrons must have moved along the wire from the negatively-charged body to the positively-charged one in order to discharge the two objects. There must have been a flow of electron current through the wire.

Anything which causes an electron flow through a conductor is called an **electromotive force (e.m.f)**. The more modern term is voltage. This term will be used to represent e.m.f. Each excess electron does not flow all the way through the conductor to the point of electron deficiency. It is more like the maneuver in croquet when you try to knock your opponent's ball out.

In this case you hold your foot on your own ball so it won't move. But when you smack it with the mallet, the opposing ball which was lying next to it goes flying. You could do the same thing with a whole string of croquet balls in line, if you wanted to. Remember our billiard ball explanation in *Chapter 3*?

Conductors, Resistors and Insulators

This same kind of chain reaction occurs in a **conductor**. An electron near one end strikes another. That in turn, hits still another, and so on until the effect is felt all the way down the line. No one electron moves very far, but the effect of the electron flow is felt at all points along the conductor.

If we connect the ends of a copper wire (a conductor) to the positive and negative terminals of a battery, a fairly sizable **electron current** will flow. If we connect a piece of carbon rod across these same terminals, the current will be much less. If we touch a piece of glass to the terminals, no current will flow at all. *Obviously some materials are better conductors than others.*

It appears that the better conductors are those, such as *gold, silver and aluminum*, whose atoms readily give up an electron from its outer shell or orbit. (N5B07)

Some materials hold on to their electrons so tightly that it is difficult to free any and cause them to move along in a given direction. These are called insulators and restrict or prevent the flow of electricity. Examples of poor

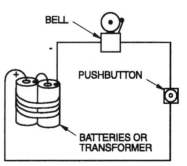

Figure 5-1 One of the most basic circuits is that of the doorbell.

conductors (and good insulators) would be *glass, air, plastic and porcelain.* (N5B08)

Depending upon how strongly the atoms hold on to their outer electrons, various materials are called, **conductors**, **resistors** or **insulators**.

Combinations of components are called **circuits**. One of the most basic circuits, the doorbell, is shown in *Figure 5-1*. The button, or switch, opens and closes the circuit. When you press the button, the circuit is closed or completed and the battery forces electrons to flow through the bell, which rings. When electrons go rushing through an electronic circuit, they do so because they are being pushed. Something is putting the pressure on them to move. The pressure is the voltage (e.m.f.) discussed earlier. This concept is very similar to the water pressure in a pipe. The greater the voltage, the more electrons will flow. If you were to short circuit the two battery terminals with a screwdriver, a large number of electrons would also flow.

To get some idea of the fantastic number of electrons which are in motion when even small currents flow, consider this. When the voltage is great enough to send a current of one ampere through a wire, 6,280,000,000,000,000,000 electrons pass a given point every single second! You don't need to memorize this number, by the way. You will not be asked it in a test question.

There are many methods known for generating a voltage, but the two most commonly used are **chemical** and **electromagnetic**. The first is the basis of *cells and batteries*. The second method is the basis of *electric generators*.

Alternating Current

Up to this point we have discussed direct current (DC) which flows in only one direction in a conductor. However, you should be familiar with **alternating current** (**AC**). This is an electron flow which periodically reverses itself and *flows in both directions*. Alternating current appears in power lines, audio and radio frequency (RF) generators. (N5C10)(N5C11)

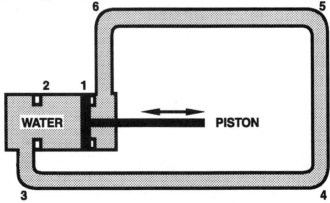

Figure 5-2 Water analogies can often be used to simulate the action of an electric current. In this drawing, the action of alternating current is shown.

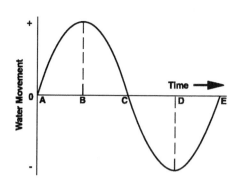

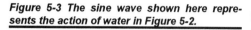

Figure 5-3 The sine wave shown here represents the action of water in Figure 5-2.

Current flow is, in many ways, like the flow of water. A hydraulic analogy will help in understanding the basic AC concept. In *Figure 5-2* we see how a piston, with a back and forth movement, could cause water in a closed circuit to reverse direction.

When the piston moves from 1 to 2, water will be pushed ahead of it and will close in behind it. The flow in the circuit will move in the direction 3-4-5-6, which represents the time A-B-C in *Figure 5-3*. When the piston reaches the end of its travel (position 2 in *Figure 5-2* and point C in *Figure 5-3*), it will reverse direction. But note that at the instant of reversal, both the piston motion and the water flow have stopped. Then the piston starts moving from 2 to 1, and the water now flows around 6-5-4-3. This represents C-D-E in *Figure 5-3*.

Alternating current flow is very similar. Imagine that "water movement" in *Figure 5-2* is really current flow. The current starts at zero state of flow (A) and gradually increases in strength until it reaches a maximum in one direction (B). Then it gradually decreases until it stops altogether (C). Next, it increases to a maximum in the opposite direction (D), finally decreasing again back to zero (E).

Electricity which behaves in this manner is called **alternating current** or **AC**. This complete series of events is called a **cycle**. The number of these cycles which occur during a period of one second is said to be the **frequency** of the AC. As mentioned in *Chapter A*, we honor Herr Heinrich Hertz by calling this complete sequence a **Hertz**. (N5D01)(N5D02)

Until now we have been talking about rate of current flow. But we already know that any such flow must have a propelling force. The force behind electron flow is our old friend **voltage**. The way in which an AC voltage changes with time is the same as for current as shown in *Figure 5-3*. The result of this action is called an **AC sine wave**. *This waveform is basic to virtually every piece of radio equipment.*

If the time it takes the voltage to travel from A to E is 1/60 second, then the frequency of this particular voltage would be 60 cycles (or Hertz) per second. Ordinary power lines in this country are standardized at a frequency of 60 Hertz (Hz) at a voltage of 120. That's the voltage available at the wall outlets in your home or apartment. In England the standard voltage is 240 with a frequency of 50 Hz. (N5B06)(N5D11)

Do you remember the example in *Chapter 3*, where you threw a rock in a still pond of water? If we could view the action of the waves from a side position, the wave action would look exactly like the sine waveform in *Figure 5-3*. There are three characteristics of a sine wave that you should be aware of. They are the: (1) amplitude, (2) wavelength, and (3) frequency.

The vertical distance between the crest and the trough is the **amplitude** of the wave. The bigger the rock, the larger the amplitude of the wave. If you toss a Volkswagen in the quiet pool, larger waves will be created than for a small pebble.

The distance between any two reference points (for example between two crests or two troughs) is the length of the wave or, more commonly, the **wavelength**. The number of times a crest (or a valley) passes a given point in a specific length of time is called the **frequency**. These repetitive cycles must be related to time. The most common unit of time is the second. Thus, frequency is expressed in the number of cycles per second (actually Hertz per second or simply Hz). (N5D08)

You should be able to visualize the relationship between frequency and wavelength. As frequency is increased, wavelength decreases. Conversely, as wavelength increases, the frequency of the wave must decrease. (N5D09)(N5D10)

Remember, the number of sine wave events which occur each second is referred to as the frequency. The distance or length between any two identical and repetitive reference points on a sine wave is called the wavelength.

Welcome To Math Class—Be Seated

By using a water analogy in *Chapter 3*, you may have been given the impression that a cycle was a slow and ponderous event. Nothing could be further from the truth. Sine wave frequencies are usually generated electronically rather than mechanically and the alternations occur very rapidly. For example, the radio frequencies generated by a cellular telephone alternate more than 800 million times per second (800 mega-Hertz). Think that's fast? Home satellite receivers operate at frequencies four times as high!

The lowest frequencies with which hams are involved are called audio frequencies. This is the range between 20 Hz and 20,000 Hz (20 kHz) that our ears can hear. Above 20,000 Hz, the spectrum is usually referred to as radio frequencies. The various radio frequency sub-definitions were mentioned in *Chapter 1*. (N5D03)(N5D04)(N5D05)(N5D06)

Why is it important to understand mathematics, such as the difference between wavelength and frequency? Let's say a friend makes a schedule to talk with you on 10 meters (wavelength), but your receiver is calibrated in Mhz (frequency). How do you make the conversion?

There are 1,000 Hertz (Hz) in a kiloHertz (kHz). Likewise, there are a million Hertz or a 1,000 kiloHertz in a megaHertz (MHz). Ten times one hundred kiloHertz is also equals one MHz. The largest unit you will be expected to deal with is the gigaHertz (GHz). There are 1,000 megaHertz in one gigaHertz. Remember, these are the rates of the alternating radio frequency energy—a gigaHertz is 1,000 million times per second! (N5A09)(N5A10)

Remember centi means 100, milli means 1,000, and mega means one million. You will be using these multipliers throughout your Amateur Radio career.

What if your "Helping Ham" friend called you on the telephone and said there was a rare DX station on 7,125 kiloHertz. Your dial is calibrated in megaHertz. Where would you find the station? Remember, there are 1,000 kHz in one MHz. But the frequency you are looking for is more than seven times as much or 7,000 kHz. Since there are 1,000 kHzs in one MHz, the answer is more than 7 MHz. Thus, from the available answers in the test question, the answer must be 7.125 MHz. (N5A01)

Using the same analysis, determine what 3.525 MHz would be in kHz. Or convert 3,725 kHz to Hertz. (The correct answers are 3525 kHz and 3,725,000 Hertz, respectively). (N5A02)(N5A03)(N5D07)

If the meter on your transmitter was calibrated in *milli*amperes, how many amperes would be flowing if the meter indicated 3,000 milliamperes? Remember, "milli" means one thousand. Thus, there are 1,000 milliamperes in one ampere. By dividing 1,000 into 3,000 we arrive at the answer of 3 amperes. (N5A05)

Milli is milli, regardless of how it is used. Another question on metering in the test asks how many volts there are in 3,500 *milli*volts. There are 1,000 millivolts in a volt so the correct answer is 3.5 volts. (N5A06)

We can use decimal conversion when calculating power. For example, there are 1,000 *milli*watts in a watt. Thus, a hand-held transceiver which puts out 500 milli-watts (500 is half of one thousand) is producing one-half watt. (N5A11)

Capacitor values confuse the best of us, even with an Amateur license. We usually wind up with a pencil and paper moving decimal points around with great abandon. The smallest common unit of capacity is the pico-farad. There are 1,000 pico's in a nano-farad (1,000 pF equals one nF). There are also 1,000 nano-farads in a micro-farad. Thus, if we multiply 1,000 pico-farads in a nano-farad by 1,000 nano-farads in a micro-farad, we find there are 1,000,000 pico-farads in one micro-farad. Finally, there are one-million micro-farads in a farad. Thus, 500,000 micro-farads would be a half-farad (0.5 F). (N5A07)(N5A08)

You also need to understand how to convert *metric measurements*. What if an antenna drawing specifies a wire 400 centimeters long. How long is this in meters or feet? Remember that "centi" means hundred. Thus, there are four units of 100 in a something that is 400 centimeters long. In this case the four units is the measurement in meters. Thus the antenna 400 centimeters long would be four meters long. (N5A04)

Like it or not, Mathematics is an important part of our hobby. Here's another aspect of math that is used in Amateur Radio.

The Law According To Mr. Ohm

Voltage (e.m.f.) tends to force electrons through a wire. When this happens, we say there is a current flow in the wire. The amount of current is expressed in *amperes*. (N5B02)(N5B03)

There will always be some opposition to the flow or current. *There is no such thing as a perfect conductor.* Every circuit element has some **resistance**. But when it is specifically desired to oppose or limit the current (the flow of electrons) to a certain value, a component known as a **resistor** is installed. It is neither a good conductor or a good insulator. The properties of a resistor lie somewhere in between the two extremes depending on the resistance value. (T5A01)

Resistors come in all sizes and shapes, and their ability to oppose or limit electron current flow (or resistance) is expressed in a basic unit called the **ohm**. By international agreement, the ohm is designated as the opposition offered to a steady current by a column of mercury of specified dimensions. (N5B10)(N5B11)

The basic unit of voltage is described by the basic term **volts**. *Voltage is the pressure causing the flow of electrons.* The volt is simply that amount of electrical pressure which will drive a current of one ampere through a resistance of one ohm. From this definition it is obvious that there is a close relationship between volts, ohms and amperes. (N5B01)(N5B04)

Figure 5-4 You will always remember Ohm's Law if you commit this drawing to memory.

If the voltage increases, we would expect the current to go up also. But if the *resistance increases* there will be more opposition to flow and *the current will drop.* These relationships were expressed in three little mathematical formulas over 150 years ago by a German physicist, Georg Simon Ohm, after whom they are called **Ohm's Law.** This is one of the most important of all electrical relationships for voltage, current and resistance in a circuit. (N5C01)(T5B01)

Figure 5-4 shows Mr. Ohm's law in a graphic way. We have adopted the letter symbol (I or intensity) for the current in amperes, (V) for the voltage, and (R) for the resistance in ohms. The chart in *Figure 5-4* is laid out in the manner shown for a very specific reason. If you cover the value you want to know with your fingertip, the remaining two symbols become the formula used to determine the answer.

How do you find the current in amperes in any circuit? Cover the I with your fingertip, which leaves V over R. Therefore you must divide the voltage by the resistance in ohms to find the value of current (I). Thus the formula becomes *(I) equals (V) divided by (R)*. By the same token we can see that *(R) equals (V) divided by (I)*. Finally, from *Figure 5-4*, we can deduce that *(V) equals (I) times (R)*. (T5B02)(T5B03) (T5B04)(T5B11)

As a practical example of how this works, let's find out how much current a light bulb having a filament resistance of 100 ohms will pass when it is connected to a source of 200 volts. The formula says that *current (I) in amperes equals voltage (V) divided by resistance(R)*. Thus 200 divided by 100 equals 2 amperes. (N5C03)

If a 4,800 ohm resistor (4.8K ohm) is connected to 120 volts, approximately how much current will flow through it? Divide 4,800 into 120 and the answer is 0.025 amperes or (move the decimal three places to the right for milli) 25 milliamperes. If the resistor is 10 times greater resistance (48,000 ohms), what would the current be? This one is easy. Even without calculating the value, you know that the current would be one-tenth or 2.5 milliamperes. (T5B07)(T5B08)

If the same 48,000 ohm resistor is connected to 12 volts (one-tenth the voltage in the previous example), what current would flow through it? In this case, divide 48,000 into 12 for an answer of 0.00025. This is 0.25 milliamperes or, more correctly 250 microamperes (uA). *A micro is one-thousandth of a milli.*

The voltage relationship in Ohm's Law is similar. If a meter connected in series with a 50 ohm resistor shows a current of 2 amperes, how much voltage will develop across the resistor? By multiplying the current (in amperes) by the resistance *(V = I times R)*, the answer is found to be 100 volts. (N5C02)(N5C04)

Here's the sort of puzzle you might run into everyday as an auto mechanic. Consider this case where the resistance and current are known, and the voltage must be found. Say we have a parking light bulb which has an operating resistance of 4 ohms. When lit to full brilliance it draws a current of 1.5 amperes. Can we use this lamp in a circuit where it will have 12 volts placed across it? Remember, *Figure 5-4* tells us the formula is *V equals I times R*. If we multiply 4 ohms by 1.5 amperes, the answer turns out to be 6 volts. If we insert a 6-volt lamp into the socket, it would quickly burn out with 12 volts impressed across it. Thus the answer is no. This light bulb would be used in an automobile which uses a standard 12 volt battery. (N5B05)

Suppose we want to determine the resistance when the voltage and current is known. For example, if a 12-volt battery supplies 0.25 amperes to a circuit, what is the resistance of the circuit? *Remember that R equals voltage divided by current.* If we divide 12 by 0.25, the answer is 48 ohms. If the same battery supplies 0.15 amperes to a circuit, the resistance of the circuit must be 80 ohms. (T5B05)(T5B06)

I Got The Power!

The resistor is one of the most commonly encountered components in electronic circuits. *Its primary use is to convert electrical energy into heat energy.* This heat may serve some useful purpose, such as for an electric stove. It may be wasted when the purpose of the resistor is simply to provide a needed voltage drop.

The ability to do work is called **energy**. If you chop a pile of wood, you expend energy. When a flashlight is illuminated, it consumes energy. We say the **electrical energy** is converted to heat and light. The *rate of energy use or consumption* is called **power**. A high wattage bulb in your ceiling lamp will consume energy faster than a flashlight bulb. In other words it will exhibit a *greater power consumption*. (N5C05)(N5C06)

The rate at which heat is produced when current flows through a resistor is expressed in **watts**. The watt is the *basic unit of electrical power*. The formula is (W = I squared R), where (W) is the power in watts, (I) is the current in amperes, and (R) is the resistance in ohms. (N5C07)

The watts consumed by a resistor, often called the I-squared-R loss, appear entirely as heat. It is obvious that the larger the surface area of the resistor and the freer the circulation of air around it, the more easily the heat can be dissipated. Resistors are made in a wide variety of sizes, not only in terms of resistance, but also in the amount of power they can safely handle without danger of burn-out.

If there is no current flow between the two terminals of a battery, it is said to be an **open circuit**. If there is an excessively high current between the terminals, it is caused by a **short circuit**. (N5C08)(N5C09)

Inductors

The inductance of a coil is determined by the number of turns as well as the overall size and shape. If the turns are wound around an iron core (rather than air) the inductance will increase many times, depending upon **permeability** of the core material in an inductor. The permeability of air is taken as 1, while the permeability of core materials may be many thousands of times greater. It is therefore a simple matter to *increase the inductance of a coil many times simply by providing it with a high-permeability core.*

The basic unit of inductance is the **Henry**, defined as the inductance of any circuit in which a current changing at the rate of one ampere per second will induce an e.m.f. of one volt. The symbol for inductance is the letter "**L**." The values of L encountered in electronic work vary from a few microHenries (millionths or 10-6 Henries) up to perhaps several Henries. A milliHenry is equal to 10-3 Henry. (T5A03)(T5A04)

Inductors in *series will add up in value*. If two equal value inductors are connected in parallel, the combined value will be half the value of either inductor. If unequal value inductors are connected in parallel, the combined value will be less than the lowest value inductor. (T5A08)(T5A09)

Capacitors

Still another device often found in electronic circuits is the **capacitor**. Old timers (and a few auto mechanics) call these components "condensers" but these are found in air conditioners and refrigerators. A capacitor is usually an arrangement of two or more metallic plates, separated from one another by air or some other insulating material known as a **dielectric**. Just as an inductor can store energy in a magnetic field, a capacitor can store energy in an electric field. (T5A05)

The basic unit of capacitance is the **farad**. This is the value a capacitor would have if its voltage were raised one volt by a current of one ampere for one second. Such a capacitor, however, would be physically huge. Thus a farad is almost never encountered in practice. (T5A06)(T5A07)

Multiple capacitors connected in a circuit are the mathematical opposite of resistors and inductors. *If two equal value capacitors are connected in series, the total value will be half the value of either capacitor.* If a number of capacitors are connected in series, the total value will always be less than the smallest value capacitor. By the same token, if two *equal value* capacitors are connected in parallel, the combined value will be twice the value of either capacitor. If a number of capacitors are connected in parallel, the total value will be the sum of all the capacitor values. (T5A10)(T5A11)

Clearly, you are going to have to memorize some of the equivalences mentioned in this chapter. Once you think you've got it, try answering the following questions.

Novice Subelement 5 (4 questions)

N5A01—If a dial marked in kilohertz shows a reading of 7125 kHz, what would it show if it were marked in megahertz? (A) 0.007125 MHz; (B) 7.125 MHz; (C) 71.25 MHz; (D) 7,125,000 MHz.

N5A02—If a dial marked in megahertz shows a reading of 3.525 MHz, what would it show if it were marked in kilohertz? (A) 0.003525 kHz; (B) 35.25 kHz; (C) 3525 kHz; (D) 3,525,000 kHz.

N5A03—If a dial marked in kilohertz shows a reading of 3725 kHz, what would it show if it were marked in hertz? (A) 3,725 Hz; (B) 37.25 Hz; (C) 3,725 Hz; (D) 3,725,000 Hz.

N5A04—How long is an antenna that is 400 centimeters long? (A) 0.0004 meters; (B) 4 meters; (C) 40 meters; (D) 40,000 meters.

N5A05—If an ammeter marked in amperes is used to measure a 3000-milliampere current, what reading would it show? (A) 0.003 amperes; (B) 0.3 amperes; (C) 3 amperes; (D) 3,000,000 amperes.

N5A06—If a voltmeter marked in volts is used to measure a 3500-millivolt potential, what reading would it show? (A) 0.35 volts; (B) 3.5 volts; (C) 35 volts; (D) 350 volts.

N5A07—How many farads is 500,000 microfarads? (A) 0.0005 farads; (B) 0.5 farads; (C) 500 farads; (D) 500,000,000 farads.

N5A08—How many microfarads is 1,000,000 picofarads? (A) 0.001 microfarads; (B) 1 microfarad; (C) 1,000 microfarads; (D) 1,000,000,000 microfarads.

N5A09—How many hertz are in a kilohertz? (A) 10; (B) 100; (C) 1000; (D) 1000000.

N5A10—How many kilohertz are in a megahertz? (A) 10; (B) 100; (C) 1000; (D) 1000000.

N5A11—If you have a hand held transceiver which puts out 500 milliwatts, how many watts would this be? (A) 0.02; (B) 0.5; (C) 5; (D) 50.

N5B01—What is the flow of electrons in an electric circuit called? (A) Voltage; (B) Resistance; (C) Capacitance; (D) Current.

N5B02—What is the basic unit of electric current? (A) The volt; (B) The watt; (C) The ampere; (D) The ohm.

N5B03—What is the pressure that forces electrons to flow through a circuit? (A) Magnetomotive force, or inductance; (B) Electromotive force, or voltage; (C) Farad force, or capacitance; (D) Thermal force, or heat.

N5B04—What is the basic unit of voltage? (A) The volt; (B) The watt; (C) The ampere; (D) The ohm.

N5B05—How much voltage does an automobile battery usually supply? (A) About 12 volts; (B) About 30 volts; (C) About 120 volts; (D) About 240 volts.

N5B06—How much voltage does a wall outlet usually supply (in the US)? (A) About 12 volts; (B) About 30 volts; (C) About 120 volts; (D) About 480 volts.

N5B07—What are three good electrical conductors? (A) Copper, gold, mica; (B) Gold, silver, wood; (C) Gold, silver, aluminum; (D) Copper, aluminum, paper.

N5B08—What are four good electrical insulators? (A) Glass, air, plastic, porcelain; (B) Glass, wood, copper, porcelain; (C) Paper, glass, air, aluminum; (D) Plastic, rubber, wood, carbon.

N5B09—What does an electrical insulator do? (A) It lets electricity flow through it in one direction; (B) It does not let electricity flow through it; (C) It lets electricity flow through it when light shines on it; (D) It lets electricity flow through it.

N5B10—What limits the amount of current that flows through a circuit if the voltage stays the same? (A) Reliance; (B) Reactance; (C) Saturation; (D) Resistance.

N5B11—What is the basic unit of resistance? (A) The volt; (B) The watt; (C) The ampere; (D) The ohm.

N5C01—What formula shows how voltage, current and resistance relate to each other in an electric circuit? (A) Ohm's Law; (B) Kirchhoff's Law; (C) Ampere's Law; (D) Tesla's Law.

N5C02—If a current of 2 amperes flows through a 50-ohm resistor, what is the voltage across the resistor? (A) 25 volts; (B) 52 volts; (C) 100 volts; (D) 200 volts.

N5C03—If a 100-ohm resistor is connected to 200 volts, what is the current through the resistor? (A) 1/2 ampere; (B) 2 amperes; (C) 300 amperes; (D) 20000 amperes.

N5C04—If a current of 3 amperes flows through a resistor connected to 90 volts, what is the resistance? (A) 30 ohms; (B) 93 ohms; (C) 270 ohms; (D) 1/30 ohm.

N5C05—What is the word used to describe how fast electrical energy is used? (A) Resistance; (B) Current; (C) Power; (D) Voltage.

N5C06—If you have light bulbs marked 60 watts, 75 watts and 100 watts, which one will use electrical energy the fastest? (A) The 60 watt bulb; (B) The 75 watt bulb; (C) The 100 watt bulb; (D) They will all be the same.

N5C07—What is the basic unit of electrical power? (A) The ohm; (B) The watt; (C) The volt; (D) The ampere.

N5C08—Which electrical circuit can have no current? (A) A closed circuit; (B) A short circuit; (C) An open circuit; (D) A complete circuit.

N5C09—Which electrical circuit uses too much current? (A) An open circuit; (B) A dead circuit; (C) A closed circuit; (D) A short circuit.

N5C10—What is the name of a current that flows only in one direction? (A) An alternating current; (B) A direct current; (C) A normal current; (D) A smooth current.

N5C11—What is the name of a current that flows back and forth, first in one direction, then in the opposite direction? (A) An alternating current; (B) A direct current; (C) A rough current; (D) A reversing current.

N5D01—What term means the number of times per second that an alternating current flows back and forth? (A) Pulse rate; (B) Speed; (C) Wavelength; (D) Frequency.

N5D02—What is the basic unit of frequency? (A) The hertz; (B) The watt; (C) The ampere; (D) The ohm.

N5D03—What frequency can humans hear? (A) 0 - 20 Hz; (B) 20 - 20,000 Hz; (C) 200 - 200,000 Hz; (D) 10,000 - 30,000 Hz.

N5D04—Why do we call signals in the range 20 Hz to 20,000 Hz audio frequencies? (A) Because the human ear cannot sense anything in this range; (B) Because the human ear can sense sounds in this range; (C) Because this range is too low for radio energy; (D) Because the human ear can sense radio waves in this range.

N5D05—What is the lowest frequency of electrical energy that is usually known as a radio frequency? (A) 20 Hz; (B) 2,000 Hz; (C) 20,000 Hz; (D) 1,000,000 Hz.

N5D06—Electrical energy at a frequency of 7125 kHz is in what frequency range? (A) Audio; (B) Radio; (C) Hyper; (D) Super-high.

N5D07—If a radio wave makes 3,725,000 cycles in one second, what does this mean? (A) The radio wave's voltage is 3,725 kilovolts; (B) The radio wave's wavelength is 3,725 kilometers; (C) The radio wave's frequency is 3,725 kilohertz; (D) The radio wave's speed is 3,725 kilometers per second.

N5D08—What is the name for the distance an AC signal travels during one complete cycle? (A) Wave speed; (B) Waveform; (C) Wavelength; (D) Wave spread.

N5D09—What happens to a signal's wavelength as its frequency increases? (A) It gets shorter; (B) It gets longer; (C) It stays the same; (D) It disappears.

N5D10—What happens to a signal's frequency as its wavelength gets longer? (A) It goes down; (B) It goes up; (C) It stays the same; (D) It disappears.

N5D11—What does 60 hertz (Hz) mean? (A) 6000 cycles per second; (B) 60 cycles per second; (C) 6000 meters per second; (D) 60 meters per second.

Technician Subelement 5 (2 questions)

T5A01—What does resistance do in an electric circuit? (A) It stores energy in a magnetic field; (B) It stores energy in an electric field; (C) It provides electrons by a chemical reaction; (D) It opposes the flow of electrons.

T5A02—What is the ability to store energy in a magnetic field called? (A) Admittance; (B) Capacitance; (C) Resistance; (D) Inductance.

T5A03—What is the basic unit of inductance? (A) The coulomb; (B) The farad; (C) The henry; (D) The ohm.

T5A04—What is a henry? (A) The basic unit of admittance; (B) The basic unit of capacitance; (C) The basic unit of inductance; (D) The basic unit of resistance.

T5A05—What is the ability to store energy in an electric field called? (A) Inductance; (B) Resistance; (C) Tolerance; (D) Capacitance.

T5A06—What is the basic unit of capacitance? (A) The farad; (B) The ohm; (C) The volt; (D) The henry.

T5A07—What is a farad? (A) The basic unit of resistance; (B) The basic unit of capacitance; (C) The basic unit of inductance; (D) The basic unit of admittance.

T5A08—If two equal-value inductors are connected in series, what is their total inductance? (A) Half the value of one inductor; (B) Twice the value of one inductor; (C) The same as the value of either inductor; (D) The value of one inductor times the value of the other.

T5A09—If two equal-value inductors are connected in parallel, what is their total inductance? (A) Half the value of one inductor; (B) Twice the value of one inductor; (C) The same as the value of either inductor; (D) The value of one inductor times the value of the other.

T5A10—If two equal-value capacitors are connected in series, what is their total capacitance? (A) Twice the value of one capacitor; (B) The same as the value of either capacitor; (C) Half the value of either capacitor; (D) The value of one capacitor times the value of the other.

T5A11—If two equal-value capacitors are connected in parallel, what is their total capacitance? (A) Twice the value of one capacitor; (B) Half the value of one capacitor; (C) The same as the value of either capacitor; (D) The value of one capacitor times the value of the other

T5B01—Ohm's Law describes the mathematical relationship between what three electrical quantities? (A) Resistance, voltage and power; (B) Current, resistance and power; (C) Current, voltage and power; (D) Resistance, current and voltage.

T5B02—How is the current in a DC circuit calculated when the voltage and resistance are known? (A) I = R x E [current equals resistance multiplied by voltage]; (B) I = R / E [current equals resistance divided by voltage]; (C) I = E / R [current equals voltage divided by resistance]; (D) I = P / E [current equals power divided by voltage].

T5B03—How is the resistance in a DC circuit calculated when the voltage and current are known? (A) R = I / E [resistance equals current divided by voltage]; (B) R = E / I [resistance equals voltage divided by current]; (C) R = I x E [resistance equals current multiplied by voltage]; (D) R = P / E [resistance equals power divided by voltage].

T5B04—How is the voltage in a DC circuit calculated when the current and resistance are known? (A) E = I / R [voltage equals current divided by resistance]; (B) E = R / I [voltage equals resistance divided by current]; (C) E = I x R [voltage equals current multiplied by resistance]; (D) E = P / I [voltage equals power divided by current].

T5B05—If a 12-volt battery supplies 0.25 ampere to a circuit, what is the circuit's resistance? (A) 0.25 ohm; (B) 3 ohm; (C) 12 ohms; (D) 48 ohms.

T5B06—If a 12-volt battery supplies 0.15 ampere to a circuit, what is the circuit's resistance? (A) 0.15 ohm; (B) 1.8 ohm; (C) 12 ohms; (D) 80 ohms.

T5B07—If a 4800-ohm resistor is connected to 120 volts, approximately how much current will flow through it? (A) 4 A; (B) 25 mA; (C) 25 A; (D) 40 MA.

T5B08—If a 48000-ohm resistor is connected to 120 volts, approximately how much current will flow through it? (A) 400 A; (B) 40 A; (C) 25 mA; (D) 2.5 mA.

T5B09—If a 4800-ohm resistor is connected to 12 volts, approximately how much current will flow through it? (A) 2.5 mA; (B) 25 mA; (C) 40 A; (D) 400 A.

T5B10—If a 48000-ohm resistor is connected to 12 volts, approximately how much current will flow through it? (A) 250 uA; (B) 250 mA; (C) 4000 mA; (D) 4000 A.

T5B11—If you know the voltage and current supplied to a circuit, what formula would you use to calculate the circuit's resistance? (A) Ohm's law; (B) Tesla's law; (C) Ampere's law; (D) Kirchoff's law.

Chapter

Circuit Components

Four of the 55 questions you will be asked on your Technician test come from the Circuit Components section of the Novice (2) and Technician (3A) question pools. In this chapter, one of your tasks will be to associate names with diagram symbols.

Most people have seen the "innards" of an electronic product. Older equipment was a maze of wires and mysterious colorful shapes. Newer electronic devices contain etched circuit boards with more mysterious and colorful objects, but much smaller and aligned in a much more orderly manner. These bits and pieces of electronic trivia are the devices which make the product function. They are called **electronic components**. Their specific names are *switches, batteries, resistors, capacitors, inductors* and so on. The combinations of these components is called a **circuit**.

The collection of components that comprises a circuit can be laced together by copper wires in a handmade product or by copper circuit traces on the etched circuit board. For each piece of electronic equipment, there is a "roadmap" of where the parts are located and how they are connected together. This guide is called a **schematic diagram**. It, along with other supporting information, tells the manufacturer exactly how the product should be assembled.

Each of the electronic components has a **schematic symbol** which is a standardized representation of the device. Anyone skilled in electronics can look at the schematic "picture" and say "That's a resistor" or "This end of the capacitor is grounded".

Symbols

Switches—If you touch the wire from a motor to a battery terminal, you are acting just like a switch. When you touch the wire to the battery and the motor runs, you

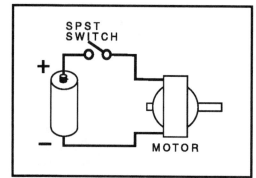

Figure 6-1 The Single Pole, Single Throw (SPST) switch used to control a motor.

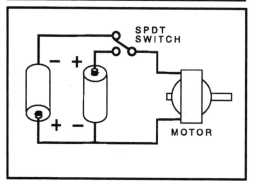

Figure 6-2 The Single Pole, Double Throw (SPDT) switch for motor direction reversal.

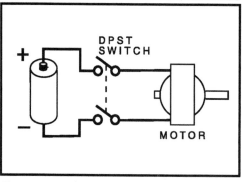

Figure 6-3 The Double Pole, Single Throw (DPST) can switch both motor leads.

have *closed* the switch. When you lift the wire, the motor stops. You have *opened* the switch. This type is called a **single-pole, single-throw (SPST)** switch. In other words, you are only breaking one wire connection. The symbol for a single-pole, single-throw (SPST) switch is shown in *Figure 6-1*. (N6A09)

In the next example, let's connect the wire to the positive terminal of one battery and then the negative terminal of a second battery. The remaining battery terminals are connected together and are wired to the common unswitched terminal of the motor. A pictorial drawing of how to accomplish this is shown in *Figure 6-2*. This will control the direction of motor rotation. In doing this, you break only one connection but you are "throwing the switch handle" (the wire you hold) in two positions. This type of switch is called a **single-pole, double-throw (SPDT)** switch. *A single-pole, double-throw switch can transfer one input line to either of two output lines.* The switch in Figure 6-2 is a SPDT. (N6A01)(N6A10)

What if you want to switch both wires between the motor and the battery off and on. This would require a single-pole, single-throw switch in series with each wire as shown in *Figure 6-3*. This is called a **double-pole, single-throw (DPST)** switch. *A DPST can switch two inputs at the same time, one input to one output, and the other input to the other output.* (N6A02)(N6A11)

You can also reverse the motor direction by switching both motor wires between two batteries. The circuit to accomplish this is illustrated in *Figure 6-4*. Let's say you have one motor wire in each hand. First you connect the two wires to the *positive and negative* terminals of battery "A" and the motor runs in one direction. Then you move the two wires over to the *negative and positive* terminals of battery "B". The motor runs in the opposite direction. In this example you have simulated a **double-pole, double-throw (DPDT)** switch. *A double-pole, double-throw switch can transfer two inputs at the same time, one input to one output and the other input to the other output.* The symbol for a double-pole, double-throw switch is used in *Figure 6-4.* (N6A12)

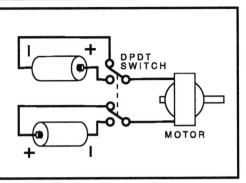

Figure 6-4 The Double Pole, Double Throw (DPDT) swtich for motor direction reversal.

The Kenwood Kids program encourages young people to become interested in Amateur Radio.

Batteries—A battery always has a *positive* and *negative* terminal. The symbol for a battery is not a round cylinder with two screw terminals on top as shown in the previous illustrations. This pictorial drawing was just a representation to illustrate a familiar object. The schematic representation of a single-cell battery is shown in *Figure 6-5.* The voltage of a single cell battery is usually around 1.5 volts. (N6A03) (N6A08)

Multiple-cell batteries, such as the 9-volt version that Radio Shack gives away with a card, are shown in schematics as illustrated in *Figure 6-6.*

The Resistor—In the last chapter, we discussed an electronic component which impeded the flow of electricity. The component was called a resistor. The primary purpose of a resistor is to limit current flow in a circuit. The electronic symbol for a resistor is shown in *Figure 6-7.* (N6A06)

In addition to their function in limiting current, resistors also convert electrical energy to heat energy. An example is the heating element in a stove or toaster. As electrical energy flows through the resistive element it is converted to heat. (T6A06)

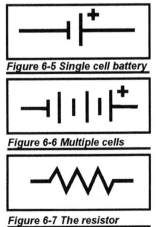

Figure 6-5 Single cell battery

Figure 6-6 Multiple cells

Figure 6-7 The resistor

There are four principal types of resistors used in electronics. They are carbon-composition, carbon-film, metal-film and wire-wound. The most common form of resistor is made from carbon. This is very much like the black material that one finds in the center of a pencil. (T6A01)

Since they do *dissipate heat* in some cases, it is necessary to observe the wattage rating of resistors. Carbon composition resistors vary in size from 1/8 watt up to 2 watts. Wire-wound resistors use nichrome wire and vary in rating from 1 watt up to several hundred watts. Usually *the physical size* is proportional to the power dissipation capability for both carbon and wire types. (T6A07)

Resistors are available in stepped values from 2.7 ohms up to 22 million ohms (22 megohms or 22M). It is difficult to accurately make a value smaller than 2.7 ohms from carbon, where there is very little use for resistors above 22M in electronic equipment.

The numeric value is not printed on the resistor. Rather, a coding scheme employing color bands is used as shown in *Figure 6-8. The first three color bands are used to indicate the resistance value.* The first two value bands are numeric indicators, while the third value band is a multiplier which indicates the number of zeros. Thus, a resistor marked red-red-orange would have a value of 22 plus three zeros, or 22,000 ohms. For small values, a black band indicates no zeros (values between 2.7 and 99 ohms). A gold band indicates divide by 10 (for values between 2.7 and 9.9 ohms). (T6A04)(T6A09)

To determine the accurate value, another factor must be known. *A fourth band indicates the tolerance* of the resistor. For example if the resistor is 100 ohms (brown-black-brown-silver), it has a *10% tolerance* as indicated by the *silver band*. The actual value of the resistor may vary between 90 and 110 ohms. This is considered a rather poor resistor. Five percent tolerance resistors are almost universal in consumer electronics equipment. Military equipment use 1% resistors. A 1% tolerance resistor has an extra value indicating band. (T6A03)(T6A05)(T6A08)(T6A10)(T6A11)

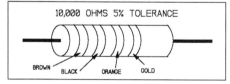

Figure 6-8 The resistor tolerance code is shown below. The first three bands are the value while the forth band is the tolerance.

Occasionally we need a version of resistor which is continuously variable. This variable resistor is called a **potentiometer**. It is simply a resistive element with a sliding contact attached to a shaft.

Figure 6-9 The potentiometer is a variable resistor.

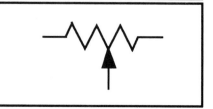

Black	0	Blue	6	Gold	5%
Brown	1	Violet	7	Silver	10%
Red	2	Grey	8	None	20%
Orange	3	White	9		
Yellow	4	Silver	0.01		
Green	5	Gold	0.1		

When the shaft position is moved, the resistance is varied. Attached to the shaft is a knob which is used as the resistance value adjustment. The symbol for a potentiometer is illustrated in *Figure 6-9*. The volume control in a radio or television is a good example of a potentiometer. (N6A04)(N6A05)(T6A02)

The Inductor—Inductors are a very special component in electronics. Every electronic product contains inductors since every wire has a small amount of inductance.

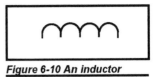

Figure 6-10 An inductor

If a piece of conducting wire is formed into a coil, it's inductance value rises dramatically. It then takes on the property of an **inductor or coil**. The symbol for an inductor or coil is shown in *Figure 6-10*.

Four parameters will effect the exact value of an inductor: (a) the core material, (b) the core diameter, (c) the length of the coil and (d) the number of turns used to wind the coil. The "core material" can be considered to be air, rather than a solid. While not directly stated, the spacing between turns will effect the inductance. The turn spacing would be a result of (c) and (d) above, combined. (T6B03)

If the number of turns are doubled, and other factors remain the same, the inductance value will increase by four times. The larger the coil, the greater the inductance value. As the spacing between turns is decreased, the inductive value is increased. Finally, the core can have a remarkable effect of the value of an inductor.

When a current is passed through an inductor, **lines of force** are created. You can demonstrate this by winding some wire on a steel nail. Connect the two wire ends to a flashlight battery and the electromagnet you have just created will attract and hold steel objects like paper clips. The intensity of the field is affected by the same factors that control inductance.

Picking up paperclips is not a unique property. Any magnet will do this. What is unique is the ability of an inductor to *store energy in its magnetic field*. Another property of inductors is they oppose the flow current, but in a very unique manner. (T6B02)

When an inductor is connected to a source of DC voltage (a battery, for example), the lines-of-force expand from the coil. But in doing so, the expanding lines cut through the turns of the coil and induce a current flow in them. However, this current flow is exactly opposite from the current caused by the battery. Thus, there is an opposition to current flow.

Eventually, however, the DC current flow reaches a maximum, the lines of force stop expanding and no opposition current is created. Thus, the current flow through the circuit is limited only by the DC resistance of the inductor. Thus *the magnetic field opposes the increase or decrease in current flow.*

Previously, it was stated that the core can have a significant effect on the value of an inductor. Here's why. The core is defined as the central portion of a coil *where the magnetic field is concentrated.* The core may consist of *air, iron, brass or other material.* So far the discussion has implied a coil of wire wound with an air core. Usually an air core coil is wound on a paper or plastic tube. (T6B01)

The lines of force in the core area can be aided or opposed if a material other than air is used for the core material. For example, if a core material of **iron** is used, the magnetic lines of force are concentrated by the material and the inductance is **increased**. The symbol used to represent an iron core inductor is illustrated in *Figure 6-11*. (T6B04)(T6B07)

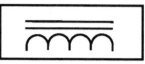

Figure 6-11 An iron core inductor

If the core material is **brass** (usually silver plated to reduce loss), the material impedes the lines of force and the inductance is **decreased** below its value with an air core.

Figure 6-12 Variable inductor

Note that in the case of either iron or brass, some losses will be introduced when used in a RF application. An air core coil will exhibit the least amount of loss.

If the iron core can be inserted and removed, the inductor can be made variable. The symbol used to represent an adjustable inductor is shown in *Figure 6-12*. The effect of the core on the inductor is illustrated in *Figure 6-13*. (T6B06)

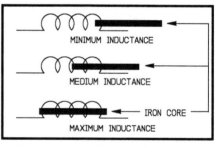

MINIMUM INDUCTANCE

MEDIUM INDUCTANCE

IRON CORE

MAXIMUM INDUCTANCE

Figure 6-13 An adjustable inductor

Most tunable coils and transformers used in electronics employ cores of powdered iron. A ceramic material called ferrite is also used to greatly increase the inductance of a coil. Virtually every piece of Amateur Radio receiving or transmitting equipment made today uses some form of adjustable inductor. (T6B06)

When adjusting a variable inductor, always use a non-metallic tool. The tool itself can change the coil's inductance and cause you to tune the variable inductor incorrectly. (T6B05)

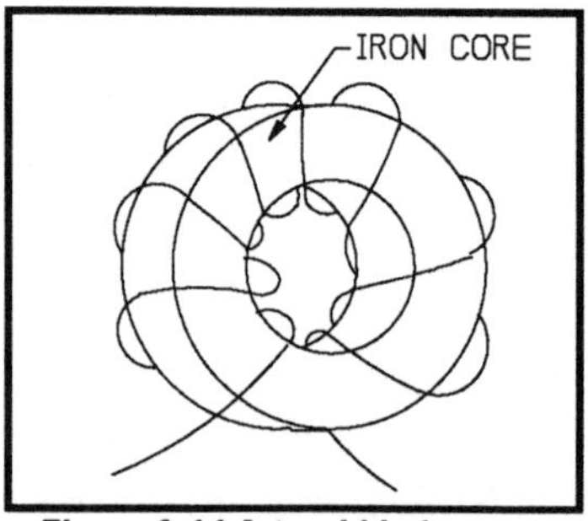

IRON CORE

Toroid—Another form of core is a donut cast of powdered iron or ferrite. The turns are wound on the donut and all the lines of force are contained in the core material. There is very little external magnetic energy. This component is called a

Figure 6-14 A toroid inductor

toroid inductor. A pictorial drawing of a toroid is shown in *Figure 6-14*. The schematic symbol is the same as for the iron core inductor which is illustrated in *Figure 6-11*. (T6B08)

The Capacitor—One of the most useful components in electronics is called a capacitor. A capacitor consists of two or more conducting plates with an insulating material between them. The insulating material can be air, paper (with or without saturating chemicals) and ceramic. The insulating medium is called the dielectric. The symbol for a capacitor is shown in *Figure 6-15*. (T6B11)

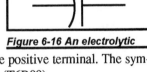

Figure 6-15 A capacitor

The characteristics of a capacitor are just the opposite of an inductor. There is no electromagnetic field associated with a capacitor. *This device stores energy, but in an electric or electrostatic field.* Also, unlike an inductor, capacitors oppose a change in voltage rather than a change in current. (T6B12)

Capacitors are specified by the capacitive value and voltage breakdown rating. The material between the plates, the area of one side of the conducting plates, the number of plates and the spacing between the plates will determine the value of the capacitor. If the size or number of plates are made *larger*, the capacitance will *increase*. If the *spacing* between the plates is *increased*, the *capacitive value decreases*. The spacing between plates and the dielectric determines the breakdown voltage of the capacitor. (T6B13)(T6B14)

If the insulator is paper, the device is referred to as a paper capacitor. By the same token, if a chemical is used in the dielectric (to increase its capacitance), the device is referred to as an electrolytic capacitor. *An electrolytic must be connected in the proper polarity.*

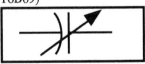

Figure 6-16 An electrolytic

Thus it's schematic diagram has a symbol indicating the positive terminal. The symbol for an electrolytic capacitor is shown in *Figure 6-16*. (T6B09)

If the spacing between plates is adjustable, the device is called a variable capacitor. The schematic diagram of a variable capacitor is given in *Figure 6-17*. (T6B10)

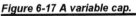

Figure 6-17 A variable cap.

Fuses—Each of us has probably changed a fuse at one time or another. Most pieces of electronic equipment contain these tiny protectors of the electronic kingdom. The symbol for a fuse is shown in *Figure 6-18*. (N6A07)

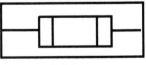

Figure 6-18 A fuse

Antenna and Ground—As mentioned elsewhere in this book, the purpose of an antenna is to radiate radio frequency energy. The schematic diagram symbol for an antenna is shown in *Figure 6-19*. (N6B03)(N6B06)

CHASSIS   EARTH   ANTENNA

Figure 6-19 Symbols for antenna and ground

One terminal of the battery (or the equipment power source) is usually common to most of the circuits in a piece of electronic equipment. We call this part of a circuit the common point or **common ground**. In older equipment, this common point was usually the metal chassis upon which the circuit was constructed.

Today, few pieces of electronic equipment use a metal chassis for the common ground. The transistor radio for example, uses one or more plastic circuit boards all contained inside a plastic enclosure. Even a large VCR in a metal case confines it's "chassis grounds" to a common length of foil running around each of the many circuit boards inside.

So the term is a little misleading. A common ground simply means the end of the circuit that is common to most of the parts of the circuit. For example, note the battery, motor and SPST switch could have been drawn as shown in the **common ground** diagram.

Obviously you don't have to go outside and drive three metal stakes into the earth to make the circuit work. Note the symbol in *Figure 6-19* called the **chassis ground**. (N6B05)

Occasionally we do need to signify an outside **earth ground**, as an example for lightning protection. We do this with a different ground symbol. The symbol denoting earth ground is also shown in *Figure 6-19*. (N6B04)

Inside a "sealed" handheld radio battery pack are individual cells, soldered in series.

Tubes and Transistors—These days, most electronic products use transistors and integrated circuits. However, vacuum tubes are still used in high-power, high voltage equipment. The symbol for a vacuum tube (in this case a triode, or three-element "valve") is shown in *Figure 6-20.* (N6B10)(N6B11)(N6B09)

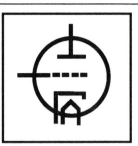

Figure 6-20 A triode vacuum tube

When you examine a schematic diagram, you are much more likely to see a transistor symbol than one for a vacuum tube. Transistors are used extensively in electronic products to amplify small signals using low voltages. (N6B01)

There are two principal types of transistors and the difference is a function of the manufacturing process. Impurities added to the silicon determine if the transistor is a negative-positive-negative (**NPN**) or a positive-negative-positive (**PNP**) device. An NPN transistor conducts electricity from a negative emitter to a positive collector when it's base voltage is made positive. The polarities for the PNP device are just the opposite. (N6B02)

The symbol for each type is shown in *Figure 6-21* and *Figure 6-22.* The only schematic difference is which way the arrow points on the element known as the emitter. It is easy to remember which is which by observing the arrow. Imagine that NPN means "not pointing in" and PNP means "pointing in pointer."(N6B07)(N6B08)

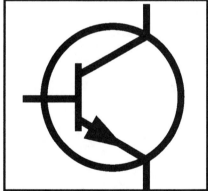

Figure 6-21 Remember the NPN by "not pointing in."

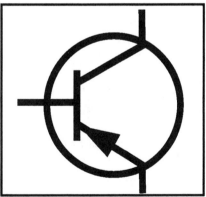

Figure 6-22 Remember the PNP by "pointing in pointer."

A popular use for inductors is the radio frequency choke from MFJ. It is useful for suppressing RF on wires and cables to prevent TV interference.

Now that you've had a look at some of the symbols used in electronics, let's see how you do with the portion of the test that asks these questions.

Novice Subelement 6 (2 questions)

N6A01—What can a single-pole, double-throw switch do? (A) It can switch one input to one output; (B) It can switch one input to either of two outputs; (C) It can switch two inputs at the same time, one input to either of two outputs, and the other input to either of two outputs; (D) It can switch two inputs at the same time, one input to one output, and the other input to another output.

N6A02—What can a double-pole, single-throw switch do? (A) It can switch one input to one output; (B) It can switch one input to either of two outputs; (C) It can switch two inputs at the same time, one input to either of two outputs, and the other input to either of two outputs; (D) It can switch two inputs at the same time, one input to one output, and the other input to the other output.

N6A03—Which component has a positive and a negative side? (A) A battery; (B) A potentiometer; (C) A fuse; (D) A resistor.

N6A04—Which component has a value that can be changed? (A) A single-cell battery; (B) A potentiometer; (C) A fuse; (D) A resistor.

N6A05—In Figure N6-1 which symbol represents a variable resistor or potentiometer? (A) Symbol 1; (B) Symbol 2; (C) Symbol 3; (D) Symbol 4.

N6A06—In Figure N6-1 which symbol represents a fixed resistor? (A) Symbol 1; (B) Symbol 2; (C) Symbol 3; (D) Symbol 4.

N6A07—In Figure N6-1 which symbol represents a fuse? (A) Symbol 1; (B) Symbol 2; (C) Symbol 3; (D) Symbol 4.

N6A08—In Figure N6-1 which symbol represents a single-cell battery? (A) Symbol 1; (B) Symbol 2; (C) Symbol 3; (D) Symbol 4.

N6A09—In Figure N6-2 which symbol represents a single-pole, single-throw switch? (A) Symbol 1; (B) Symbol 2; (C) Symbol 3; (D) Symbol 4.

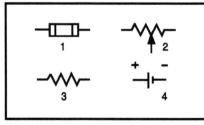

Figure N6-1

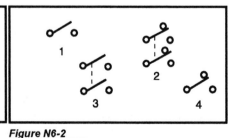

Figure N6-2

N6A10—In Figure N6-2 which symbol represents a single-pole, double-throw switch? (A) Symbol 1; (B) Symbol 2; (C) Symbol 3; (D) Symbol 4.

N6A11—In figure N6-2 which symbol represents a double-pole, single-throw switch? (A) Symbol 1; (B) Symbol 2; (C) Symbol 3; (D) Symbol 4.

N6A12—In figure N6-2 which symbol represents a double-pole, double-throw switch? (A) Symbol 1; (B) Symbol 2; (C) Symbol 3; (D) Symbol 4.

N6B01—Which component can amplify a small signal using low voltages? (A) A PNP transistor; (B) A variable resistor; (C) An electrolytic capacitor; (D) A multiple-cell battery.

N6B02—Which component conducts electricity from a negative emitter to a positive collector when its base voltage is made positive? (A) A variable resistor; (B) An NPN transistor; (C) A triode vacuum tube; (D) A multiple-cell battery.

N6B03—Which component is used to radiate radio energy? (A) An antenna; (B) An earth ground; (C) A chassis ground; (D) A potentiometer.

N6B04—In figure N6-3 which symbol represents an earth ground? (A) Symbol 1; (B) Symbol 2; (C) Symbol 3; (D) Symbol 4.

N6B05—In Figure N6-3 which symbol represents a chassis ground? (A) Symbol 1; (B) Symbol 2; (C) Symbol 3; (D) Symbol 4.

N6B06—In Figure N6-3 which symbol represents an antenna? (A) Symbol 1; (B) Symbol 2; (C) Symbol 3; (D) Symbol 4.

N6B07—In Figure N6-4 which symbol represents an NPN transistor? (A) Symbol 1; (B) Symbol 2; (C) Symbol 3; (D) Symbol 4.

N6B08—In Figure N6-4 which symbol represents a PNP transistor? (A) Symbol 1; (B) Symbol 2; (C) Symbol 3; (D) Symbol 4.

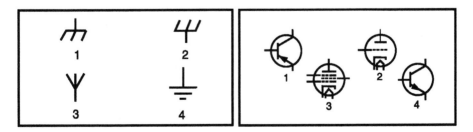

Figure N6-3

Figure N6-4

N6B09—In figure N6-4 which symbol represents a triode vacuum tube? (A) Symbol 1; (B) Symbol 2; (C) Symbol 3; (D) Symbol 4.

N6B10—What is one reason a triode vacuum tube might be used instead of a transistor in a circuit? (A) It handles higher power; (B) It uses lower voltages; (C) It uses less current; (D) It is much smaller.

N6B11—Which component can amplify a small signal but must use high voltages? (A) A transistor; (B) An electrolytic capacitor; (C) A vacuum tube; (D) A multiple-cell battery

Technician Subelement 6 (2 questions)

T6A01—What are the most common resistor types? (A) Plastic and porcelain; (B) Film and wire-wound; (C) Electrolytic and metal-film; (D) Iron core and brass core.

T6A02—What does a variable resistor or potentiometer do? (A) Its resistance changes when AC is applied to it; (B) It transforms a variable voltage into a constant voltage; (C) Its resistance changes when its slide or contact is moved; (D) Its resistance changes when it is heated.

T6A03—How do you find a resistor's tolerance rating? (A) By using a voltmeter; (B) By reading the resistor's color code; (C) By using Thevenin's theorem for resistors; (D) By reading its Baudot code.

T6A04—What do the first three color bands on a resistor indicate? (A) The value of the resistor in ohms; (B) The resistance tolerance in percent; (C) The power rating in watts; (D) The resistance material.

T6A05—What does the fourth color band on a resistor indicate? (A) The value of the resistor in ohms; (B) The resistance tolerance in percent; (C) The power rating in watts; (D) The resistance material.

T6A06—Why do resistors sometimes get hot when in use? (A) Some electrical energy passing through them is lost as heat; (B) Their reactance makes them heat up; (C) Hotter circuit components nearby heat them up; (D) They absorb magnetic energy which makes them hot.

T6A07—Why would a large size resistor be used instead of a smaller one of the same resistance? (A) For better response time; (B) For a higher current gain; (C) For greater power dissipation; (D) For less impedance in the circuit.

T6A08—What are the possible values of a 100-ohm resistor with a 10% tolerance? (A) 90 to 100 ohms; (B) 10 to 100 ohms; (C) 90 to 110 ohms; (D) 80 to 120 ohms.

T6A09—How do you find a resistor's value? (A) By using a voltmeter; (B) By using the resistor's color code; (C) By using Thevenin's therom for resistors; (D) By using the Baudot code.

T6A10—Which tolerance rating would a high-quality resistor have? (A) 0.1%; (B) 5%; (C) 10%; (D) 20%.

T6A11—Which tolerance rating would a low-quality resistor have? (A) 0.1%; (B) 5%; (C) 10%; (D) 20%.

T6B01—What is an inductor core? (A) The place where a coil is tapped for resonance; (B) A tight coil of wire used in a transformer; (C) Insulating material placed between the wires of a transformer; (D) The place inside an inductor where its magnetic field is concentrated.

T6B02—What does an inductor do? (A) It stores a charge electrostatically and opposes a change in voltage; (B) It stores a charge electrochemically and opposes a change in current; (C) It stores a charge electromagnetically and opposes a change in current; (D) It stores a charge electromechanically and opposes a change in voltage.

T6B03—What determines the inductance of a coil? (A) The core material, the core diameter, the length of the coil and whether the coil is mounted horizontally or vertically; (B) The core diameter, the number of turns of wire used to wind the coil and the type of metal used for the wire; (C) The core material, the number of turns used to wind the core and the frequency of the current through the coil; (D) The core material, the core diameter, the length of the coil and the number of turns of wire used to wind the coil.

T6B04—As an iron core is inserted in a coil, what happens to the coil's inductance? (A) It increases; (B) It decreases; (C) It stays the same; (D) It disappears.

T6B05—What can happen if you tune a ferrite-core coil with a metal tool? (A) The metal tool can change the coil's inductance and cause you to tune the coil incorrectly; (B) The metal tool can become magnetized so much that you might not be able to remove it from the coil; (C) The metal tool can pick up enough magnetic energy to become very hot; (D) The metal tool can pick up enough magnetic energy to become a shock hazard.

T6B06—In figure T6-1 which symbol represents an adjustable inductor? (A) Symbol 1; (B) Symbol 2; (C) Symbol 3; (D) Symbol 4.

T6B07—In Figure T6-1 which symbol represents an iron-core inductor? (A) Symbol 1; (B) Symbol 2; (C) Symbol 3; (D) Symbol 4.

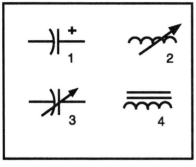

Figure T6-1

T6B08—In Figure T6-1 which symbol represents an inductor wound over a toroidal core? (A) Symbol 1; (B) Symbol 2; (C) Symbol 3; (D) Symbol 4.

T6B09—In Figure T6-1 which symbol represents an electrolytic capacitor? (A) Symbol 1; (B) Symbol 2; (C) Symbol 3; (D) Symbol 4.

T6B10—In figure T6-1 which symbol represents a variable capacitor? (A) Symbol 1; (B) Symbol 2; (C) Symbol 3; (D) Symbol 4.

T6B11—What describes a capacitor? (A) Two or more layers of silicon material with an insulating material between them; (B) The wire used in the winding and the core material; (C) Two or more conductive plates with an insulating material between them; (D) Two or more insulating plates with a conductive material between them.

T6B12—What does a capacitor do? (A) It stores a charge electrochemically and opposes a change in current; (B) It stores a charge electrostatically and opposes a change in voltage; (C) It stores a charge electromagnetically and opposes a change in current; (D) It stores a charge electromechanically and opposes a change in voltage.

T6B13—What determines the capacitance of a capacitor? (A) The material between the plates, the area of one side of one plate, the number of plates and the spacing between the plates; (B) The material between the plates, the number of plates and the size of the wires connected to the plates; (C) The number of plates, the spacing between the plates and whether the dielectric material is N type or P type; (D) The material between the plates, the area of one plate, the number of plates and the material used for the protective coating.

T6B14—As the plate area of a capacitor is increased, what happens to its capacitance? (A) It decreases; (B) It increases; (C) It stays the same; (D) It disappears.

Chapter

Practical Circuits

This chapter tests you on recognition of various elements in a simplified schematic and their relationship to each other. You will be asked two questions from the Novice pool (2) and one question from the Technician pool (3A).

In *Chapter 6* you saw how electronic components could be connected together to form a **schematic diagram**. It is not always necessary to have such detailed drawings of electronic circuitry to provide useful information, however.

Rather, the various circuits which make up a transmitter can be illustrated with a rectangle marked "transmitter". A combination of these boxes and an illustration of the connecting paths is called a **block diagram**.

Block Diagrams—Simplified Schematics

Figure N7-1 (see page 155) shows a typical block diagram. In this drawing, block 1 is an Amateur transceiver and block 3 is a dummy antenna. As we discussed in Operating Procedures (*Chapter 2*), tune-up of the transmitter should never be done into an antenna. Tuning should be done into a dummy antenna to avoid interfering with other Amateurs. The unidentified block connected between the antenna and the dummy load is called an **antenna switch.** It allows the user to switch between the antenna and the dummy load for tune-up. (N7A09)

An antenna switch can also be used to connect an antenna between a receiver and transmitter, if separate units are used rather than a transceiver. In this case, the switch should be connected properly so that the output of the transmitter can never be connected to the receiver. If the transmtter is misconnected, it's power will damage the input circuits of the receiver. (N7A06)

Another block diagram is shown in *Figure N7-2*. In this case, block 2 is an SWR meter and block 3 is an **antenna switch**. Depending on the position of this switch, the radio frequency power can be delivered to one of several antennas or a dummy load. The device which delivers the power, shown in block 1, is a transceiver. (N7A01)(N7A10)

An Amateur antenna is not always perfect. It may be used on frequencies where it is not dimensionally optimum. As mentioned in *Chapter 4*, this causes standing waves on the feed line (also called the transmission line). The feed line is used to connect the transceiver to the antenna. (N7A03)

In this case a device is required for matching the 50 ohm output of the transmitter to the value of the antenna at any given frequency. The solution to standing waves is to employ a device called an **antenna tuner** or coupler. This device matches a transceiver to a mismatched antenna system. Essentially, it fools the transceiver into thinking it is connected to a perfect antenna. (N7A02)(N7A08)

A block diagram of how to properly connect an antenna tuner is shown in *Figure N7-3*. In this diagram, block 1 is a transceiver and block 2 is an SWR meter. The block connected to the antenna represents the antenna tuner. (N7A11)

If you use an antenna tuner or several types of antennas, you must have an SWR meter connected between the transmitter output and the antenna tuner or antenna switch, as shown in *Figure N7-3*. The SWR meter tells you if the antennas are working properly and can be used when adjusting the tuner for minimum standing waves on the feed line. (N7A04)(N7A05)

Power Sources

Most Amateur transmitting and receiving equipment is designed to operate from a source of 12 volts direct current. This is true even if the equipment is used in the home rather than in an automobile.

Since few homes have a source of 12 volts DC, it is necessary to use a conversion device, called a **power supply**, if you want to use your mobile rig in your house. The power supply takes the household current from the wall outlet (120 volts AC) and changes it to 12 volts DC. (N7A12)

By the way, if your mobile transceiver worked fine in the car, but refused to work on the power supply in your house, what would you check first? The *power supply* might not be plugged in or turned on, or may actually be defective. (N7A07)

Power supplies can vary from small to enormous. For example, the power supply for a hand-held transceiver is quite tiny—its just a few batteries. A typical Amateur high frequency transceiver draws 30 amperes or more current. A heavy duty supply for this equipment would be relatively large and heavy. (N7A13)

Accessories

One of the most popular accessories found in the "ham shack" is the telegraph key. It is used for sending Morse code on the station transceiver. (N7B01)(N7B02)

The telegraph key is a manual device and the user must form the "dits" and "dahs" with their hand. True CW operators prefer to use an **electronic keyer**. A keyer is a device that delivers electronically timed "dits" and "dahs" and helps one send perfect Morse code characters. (N7B03)

Those who operate voice on their transceiver require a good quality microphone. Most transceivers have a multi-pin jack on the front panel for connecting the microphone. (N7B04)(N7B05)

Digital Configurations

RTTY—The earliest "digital" stations were called **radio teletype (RTTY)**. A five-bit code of ones and zeros called Baudot (bah-doe) was used for RTTY. This mode of operation was very popular with Amateurs since anyone could get on RTTY. The **teleprinter** machines (similar to an electronic typewriter) were donated to Amateur groups by Western Union and RCA. In the early part of the '80's, the teleprinters were replaced by computers. All that was required to make the RTTY teleprinter (or it's computer equivalent) come to life was a **modem (modulator-demodulator)** called a **terminal unit** or **TU**. (N7B06)(N7B07)(N7B10)

Packet—With the development of **packet radio**, the Amateur RTTY station was doomed to obsolescence. Packet permits addressing messages and passing them for long distance through a system of **terminal-node controllers (TNC)** or **digipeaters**. The TNC, which connects between the computer and the transceiver, is very much like an intelligent modem and permits error-free communications. Modems are used on RTTY and TNC's are used for packet communication. (N7B08)(N7B09)(N7B11)

How To Get Started in-Packet Radio from NARA

Filters

A low-pass filter (*Figure 7-1*) is found in the antenna circuit of virtually every Amateur transmitter or transceiver. The low-pass filter reduces the amount of transmitted "crud" (a new technical term for harmonics and spurious signals) below the level mandated by the FCC. The cutoff frequency would be above the transmitter output frequency. The LPF blocks the output of any harmonic or spurious frequencies above it's cutoff point. (T7A01)

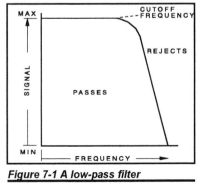

Figure 7-1 A low-pass filter

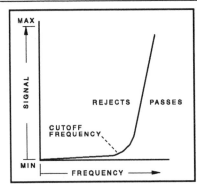

Figure 7-2 The high-pass filter

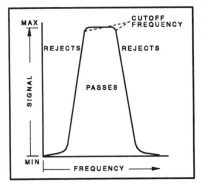

Figure 7-3 The bandpass filter

The reciprocal configuration is called a **high-pass filter**. The high-pass filter also has a reciprocal application. It would be used at the television receiver rather than at the Amateur transmitter. The corner or cutoff frequency is chosen to pass television transmissions but reject low frequency Amateur transmissions.

A low-pass and a high-pass filter can be combined to form a **band-pass filter**. RF energy is rejected above and below the frequencies the filter is designed to pass. Bandpass filters are used in virtually every Amateur transmitter, receiver and transceiver to pass certain frequencies and reject others. (T7A02)(T7A03)

Equipment Block Diagrams

Figure T7-1 (see page 158) illustrates the basic components of an Amateur transmitter. The unlabeled block is the source of radio frequency energy. It can be either a **variable frequency oscillator (VFO)** or a single frequency crystal oscillator. If the block is a VFO, this would be referred to as a *VFO controlled transmitter*. The driver and power amplifier (controlled by the telegraph key) increases the signal level of the VFO to the power where it can be effectively radiated by the antenna. (T7A05)(T7A08)

The block diagram in *Figure T7-2* (see page 158) shows a simple CW-SSB receiver. Signals received by the antenna are selected by the oscillator, amplified by the intermediate frequency amplifier stage(s) and passed to the unlabeled block. This circuit is a **detector** which converts the received radio frequency energy back to its original audio component. *Every receiver incorporates some form of detector*. In the case of a CW-SSB receiver, the signal from the beat frequency oscillator is displaced slightly from the incoming signal to produce an audio beat note. (T7A04)(T7A09)

A simplified *frequency-modulation (FM) receiver* is shown in *Figure T7-3* (see page 158). The limiter clips the amplitude of the incoming signal to reduce static and unwanted amplitude variations. The frequency discriminator produces audio output whenever the incoming frequency varies above and below a nominal value. In this circuit, the **frequency discriminator** functions as the detector. (T7A07)(T7A10)

A *frequency modulation transmitter* is illustrated in *Figure T7-4* (see page 158). In this block diagram, the unlabeled block is the circuitry that causes the phase of the radio frequency signal from the crytal oscillator to vary with modulation supplied the microphone audio amplfier. This phase shifter is called a reactance modulator. (T7A11)

Now, let's take a look at the test questions for this chapter, and refer to the block diagrams previously discussed.

Novice Subelement 7 (2 questions)

N7A01—What would you connect to your transceiver if you wanted to switch it between more than one type of antenna? (A) A terminal-node switch; (B) An antenna switch; (C) A telegraph key switch; (D) A high-pass filter.

N7A02—What device might allow use of an antenna on a band it was not designed for? (A) An SWR meter; (B) A low-pass filter; (C) An antenna tuner; (D) A high-pass filter.

N7A03—What connects your transceiver to your antenna? (A) A dummy load; (B) A ground wire; (C) The power cord; (D) A feed line.

N7A04—What might you connect between your transceiver and an antenna switch connected to several types of antennas? (A) A high-pass filter; (B) An SWR meter; (C) A key click filter; (D) A mixer.

N7A05—If your SWR meter is connected to an antenna tuner on one side, what would you connect to the other side of it? (A) A power supply; (B) An antenna; (C) An antenna switch; (D) A transceiver.

N7A06—Which of these should never be connected to the output of a transceiver? (A) An antenna switch; (B) An SWR meter; (C) An antenna; (D) A receiver.

N7A07—If your mobile transceiver works in your car but not in your home, what should you check first? (A) The power supply; (B) The speaker; (C) The microphone; (D) The SWR meter.

N7A08—What does an antenna tuner do? (A) It matches a transceiver to a mismatched antenna system; (B) It helps a receiver automatically tune in stations that are far away; (C) It switches an antenna system to a transceiver when sending, and to a receiver when listening; (D) It switches a transceiver between different kinds of antennas connectedto one feed line.

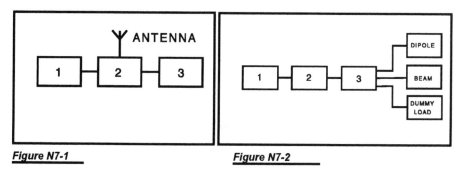

Figure N7-1   *Figure N7-2*

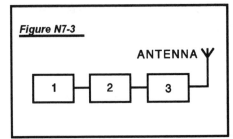

Figure N7-3

ANTENNA

1 — 2 — 3

N7A09—In Figure N7-1, if block 1 is a transceiver and block 3 is a dummy antenna what is block 2? (A) A terminal-node switch; (B) An antenna switch; (C) A telegraph key switch; (D) A high-pass filter.

N7A10—In Figure N7-2, if block 2 is an SWR meter and block 3 is an antenna switch, what is block 1? (A) A transceiver; (B) A high-pass filter; (C) An antenna tuner; (D) A modem.

N7A11—In Figure N7-3, if block 1 is a transceiver and block 2 is an SWR meter, what is block 3? (A) An antenna switch; (B) An antenna tuner; (C) A key-click filter; (D) A terminal-node controller.

N7A12—What device converts household current to 12 VDC? (A) A catalytic converter; (B) A low-pass filter; (C) A power supply; (D) An RS-232 interface.

N7A13—Which of these usually needs a heavy-duty power supply? (A) An SWR meter; (B) A receiver; (C) A transceiver; (D) An antenna switch .

N7B01—What would you connect to a transceiver to send Morse code? (A) A terminal-node controller; (B) A telegraph key; (C) An SWR meter; (D) An antenna switch.

N7B02—Where would you connect a telegraph key to send Morse code? (A) To a power supply; (B) To an antenna switch; (C) To a transceiver; (D) To an antenna.

N7B03—What do many amateurs use to help form good Morse code characters? (A) A key-operated on/off switch; (B) An electronic keyer; (C) A key-click filter; (D) A DTMF keypad.

N7B04—Where would you connect a microphone for voice operation? (A) To a power supply; (B) To an antenna switch; (C) To a transceiver; (D) To an antenna.

N7B05—What would you connect to a transceiver for voice operation? (A) A splatter filter; (B) A terminal-voice controller; (C) A receiver audio filter; (D) A microphone.

N7B06—What would you connect to a transceiver for RTTY operation? (A) A modem and a teleprinter or computer system; (B) A computer, a printer and a RTTY refresh unit; (C) A terminal voice controller; (D) A modem, a monitor and a DTMF keypad.

N7B07—What would you connect between a transceiver and a computer system or teleprinter for RTTY operation? (A) An RS-232 interface; (B) A DTMF keypad; (C) A modem; (D) A terminal-network controller.

N7B08—What would you connect between a computer system and a transceiver for packet-radio operation? (A) A terminal-node controller; (B) A DTMF keypad; (C) An SWR bridge; (D) An antenna tuner.

N7B09—Where would you connect a terminal-node controller for packet-radio operation? (A) Between your antenna and transceiver; (B) Between your computer and monitor; (C) Between your computer and transceiver; (D) Between your keyboard and computer.

N7B10—In RTTY operation, what equipment connects to a modem? (A) A DTMF keypad, a monitor and a transceiver; (B) A DTMF microphone, a monitor and a transceiver; (C) A transceiver and a terminal-network controller; (D) A transceiver and a teleprinter or computer system.

N7B11—In packet-radio operation, what equipment connects to a terminal-node controller? (A) A transceiver and a modem; (B) A transceiver and a terminal or computer system; (C) A DTMF keypad, a monitor and a transceiver; (D) A DTMF microphone, a monitor and a transceiver.

Technician Subelement 7 (1 question)

T7A01—Why do modern HF transmitters have a built-in low-pass filter in their RF output circuits? (A) To reduce RF energy below a cutoff point; (B) To reduce low-frequency interference to other amateurs; (C) To reduce harmonic radiation; (D) To reduce fundamental radiation.

T7A02—What circuit blocks RF energy above and below a certain limit? (A) A band-pass filter; (B) A high-pass filter; (C) An input filter; (D) A low-pass filter.

T7A03—What type of filter is used in the IF section of receivers to block energy outside a certain frequency range? (A) A band-pass filter; (B) A high-pass filter; (C) An input filter; (D) A low-pass filter.

T7A04—What circuit is found in all types of receivers? (A) An audio filter; (B) A beat-frequency oscillator; (C) A detector; (D) An RF amplifier.

T7A05—What circuit has a variable-frequency oscillator connected to a driver and a power amplifier? (A) A packet-radio transmitter; (B) A crystal-controlled transmitter; (C) A single-sideband transmitter; (D) A VFO-controlled transmitter.

T7A06—What circuit combines signals from an IF amplifier stage and a beat-frequency oscillator (BFO), to produce an audio signal? (A) An AGC circuit; (B) A detector circuit; (C) A power supply circuit; (D) A VFO circuit.

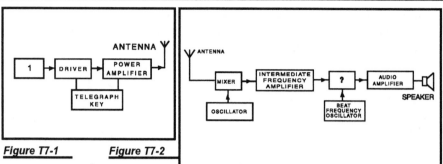

Figure T7-1   Figure T7-2

T7A07—What circuit uses a limiter and a frequency discriminator to produce an audio signal? (A) A double-conversion receiver; (B) A variable-frequency oscillator; (C) A superheterodyne receiver; (D) A FM receiver.

T7A08—What circuit is pictured in Figure T7-1 if block 1 is a variable-frequency oscillator? (A) A packet-radio transmitter; (B) A crystal-controlled transmitter; (C) A single-sideband transmitter; (D) A VFO-controlled transmitter.

T7A09—What is the unlabeled block in Figure T7-2? (A) An AGC circuit; (B) A detector; (C) A power supply; (D) A VFO circuit.

T7A10—What circuit is pictured in Figure T7-3? (A) A double-conversion receiver; (B) A variable-frequency oscillator; (C) A superheterodyne receiver; (D) An FM receiver.

T7A11—What is the unlabeled block in Figure T7-4? (A) A band-pass filter; (B) A crystal oscillator; (C) A reactance modulator; (D) A rectifier modulator.

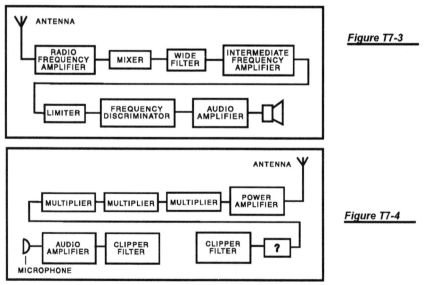

Figure T7-3

Figure T7-4

Chapter

8

Signals and Emissions

In order to insure that you understand the concept and characteristics of signals, you will be asked two questions each from Element 2 and 3A.

S ome of the terminology used in Amateur Radio has changed as a result of revisions to Part 97. As you recall, Part 97 is the section of the FCC Rules and Regulations which pertain to Amateurs.

A couple of terms have never changed since the beginning days of the Amateur Radio Service. The terms are **telegraphy** and **telephony**. Remember telegraphy means telegraph. Picture the old timer, with a transparent green brim shielding his eyes, hunched over the sounder and telegraph key sending messages down the line. To remember that telephony means voice, simply picture the telephone that you talk into each day.

Modulation

Now that you are an expert in kiloHertz, standing waves, Q-signals and so on, you should have no trouble understanding the concept of **modulation**. Modulation is defined as the *process of varying the RF energy in order to convey information*. (T8B02)

Figure 8-1 shows the basic ingredients of a typical transmitter. A crystal oscillator generates a radio frequency of high accuracy and stability. The energy is very weak and must be amplified in order to supply useful power to the antenna system. Thus the oscillator is used to drive a radio frequency power amplifier to its maximum power rating. This RF energy produced by the power amplifier is referred to as the **carrier**. If there is no modulation present on the constant-amplitude radio frequency signal, the wave is said to be *unmodulated*. An unmodulated carrier wave emission is called a *test signal*. If you were to disconnect the microphone from FM transmitter while transmitting, the carrier would be unmodulated. (T8A01)(T8B01)(T8B03)

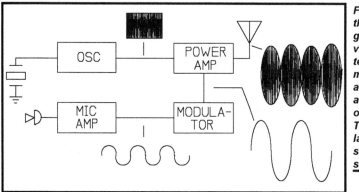

Figure 8-1 This is the block diagram for a basic voice transmitter. Notice the microphone voltage is amplified and impressed on the RF carrier. The crystal oscillator provides a stable frequency source.

Continuous Wave—If we switch the carrier on and off with a telegraph key, in an identifiable pattern such as Morse, we can modulate the carrier. This form of communications is called **CW (continuous wave)** keying. This is considered a form of amplitude modulation since the signal amplitude varies between zero and maximum. CW is the internationally accepted means of sending Morse code telegraphy messages. (N8A01)(N8A03)(T8A02)

When FM radiotelephone equipment is used for Morse code work, it is not practical to key the transmitter. Rather, the microphone is replaced by an *audio tone generator*. A tone is turned off and on with a telegraph key. This is called modulated CW or simply the emission designator **MCW.** (T8A05)(T8A11)

Radio Teletype—There is another form of modulation that does not involve voice communcations. **Radio teletype (RTTY)** is a narrow-band direct-printing form of telegraphy, as mentioned in the previous chapter. (N8A04)(T8A03)

RTTY, as well as Packet, is a form of *data communications*. Data bits consist of ones and zeros. One might assume that data can be transmitted by turning the carrier on and off. An "on" could represent a one and an "off" could represent a zero. This will actually work, but is flawed by the fact that to create a zero there is no signal. During these periods of no carrier, interference and static can cause data errors. (N8A05)(T8A04)

Frequency Shift Keying—A better method is to use a form of frequency modulation wherein a one is represented by a carrier on one frequency, and a zero by a carrier on a different or second frequency. This is called **frequency shift keying (FSK)**. With this system there is always a carrier present to suppress static and interference. (N8A02)

Audio Frequency Shift Keying—Morse, using MCW, is not the only form of intelligence that can be impressed on an FM transmitter using tones. Above 30 MHz, voice emissions are usually frequency modulation (and the emission designator is FM phone). On FM, one-zero data (such as *packet*) is transmitted by using *two audio tones* to represent the ones and zeros rather than two radio frequencies. This scheme is called **audio frequency shift keying (AFSK)**.

You can modulate your 2-meter FM transceiver to produce packet-radio emissions by connecting a terminal-node-controller to the transceiver's microphone input. (T8B04)

Amplitude Modulation—The most common form of modulating the carrier is with voice information. This is called a *phone voice emission*. The modulator in *Figure 8-1* is an audio frequency amplifier which increases the tiny voltage from the microphone and applies this voice energy to the RF power amplifier. By connecting the modulator in series with the RF power amplifier, the voltage applied to the stage (either a tube or transistor) is made to increase or decrease. In this manner, the amplified carrier energy can be amplitude modulated by the tiny voltage original produced by the microphone. (N8A06)

Figure 8-1 also shows the result of the modulation process. The carrier provides a continuous "stream" of RF energy which is sent to the antenna. The modulation applied to the RF power amplifier causes the RF output level to increase or decrease in exact proportion to the tiny microphone voltage.

From the drawing, you might conclude that the modulation causes the carrier to increase and decrease. Don't conclude this, however, because you would be 100% wrong. In actual fact, the carrier doesn't move up and down at all! The modulation voltage actually produces *additional energy* called *sidebands*.

Frequency Modulation—It is not necessary to change the amplitude of the carrier to add intelligence. The carrier can be modified in a number of other ways. For example, the frequency of the carrier wave can be varied slightly. This is called **frequency modulation phone**. Frequency modulated telephony is almost universally used on the VHF bands where Technicians operate. It is the favorite mode since it provides good audio fidelity, a strong signal relative to background noise, and is easily understood even when the signal is weak. (T8A06)(T8B05)

The amount the frequency varies with modulation is referred to as the **deviation** of the transmitter. The *louder* one speaks, *the greater the deviation*. Obviously if someone gets excited and the amplitude of the audio modulating signal is too high, the excursions or deviation of the carrier frequency can become excessive. When this happens, the signal can cause splatter and interference with adjacent channels. This is why all FM transmitters incorporate a *deviation limiter circuit*. (T8B10)(T8B11)

It is also possible to vary the phase of the radio frequency energy. It may take a bit of head-scratching to visualize the concept of **phase modulation**. You will recall that RF energy is a series of sine waves going up to positive, passing through zero and down to negative and back to zero. Picture if you will, the voice being able to vary the position of the sine wave at any given instant. In other words, in phase modulated equipment, the energy can take more or less time to reach a peak depending on the voice information impressed on the carrier by the modulator. This is what phase modulation does and the modulator to accomplish this is called a **reactance modulator**. Phase modulation is quite similar to frequency modulation and can be detected by the same type of receivers. (T8A09)(T8A10)

Single Sideband Modulation—Another popular form of modulation is called **single sideband**, suppressed carrier. This is a voice mode and is usually abbreviated as **SSB**. SSB is almost universally used for voice communication on the high frequency bands. If you operate voice on 10 meters, after receiving your Novice license or Tech-Plus CSCE, you will use SSB equipment. SSB equipment has the advantage that you can operate on either the upper or lower sideband. Upper or lower sideband means the part of the SSB signal that is above or below the suppressed carrier frequency. A technical explanation of sideband is beyond the scope of this book but will be the subject of a future NARA publication. (N8A11)(T8A07)(T8A08)

Bandwidth—From the preceding explanations you can correctly conclude that some emissions take up more spectrum space (bandwidth) than others. A CW transmitter, for example, requires the least spectrum of any signal. An RTTY signal requires less space (less than 1 kHz) than a voice signal like single sideband (between 2 and 3 kHz). Frequency modulation requires more bandwidth than any of the preceding modes (between 10 and 20 kHz). On the scale of bandwidth, from least to most, you find *CW, RTTY, SSB and FM.* Since various emissions occupy a wider frequency range (bandwidth) than others, professional communications receivers have *selectable filters to optimize reception.* Essentially the filter lets through just enough width to hold the particular emission type, and chops off the frequencies beyond that. (T8B06)(T8B07)(T8B08)

Purity of Emissions

Sometimes one hears rather "raunchy" CW signals on the Amateur bands. Using the RST scale (see *Chapter 2*), they might be graded as 5-9-0. In other words, the tone of the CW signal is terrible.

Key clicks don't count in the tone scale but they can be a problem, particularly with "home-brew" transmitters. Key clicks are caused by the sudden application or removal of power when the telegraph key is pressed and released. This creates RF emissions that start and stop very abruptly. In other words, the rise and fall times of the keying waveform are extremely fast. This will cause unwanted sidebands to be formed on both sides of the CW signal. The listener hears these sidebands as a clicking sound.

Key clicks can be completely eliminated by inserting a key click filter in the telegraph key circuitry. This is nothing more than a low pass filter. Remember, a low pass filter opposes a change in current. Thus it slows the rise and fall of the RF waveform. This eliminates the energy that causes spurious key clicks. (N8A07)

Modern transmitters and transceivers all have built in keying filters to shape and soften the transmitted signal. Today key clicks are seldom heard except from the occasional "home-brewed" transmitter where the designer has forgotten to add a suitable filter.

Another keying problem, which is still heard, is called a **chirp**. This happens when an unwanted shift of the transmitter's frequency occurs while sending Morse. If the transmitter frequency changes even a few Hz during the "dit" or "dah", it is heard at the receiving end as a "tweet" and not a pure tone. (N8A08)

This usually occurs due to an inadequately rated power supply. For example, let's say the transceiver draws 20 amperes during key-down periods. If the power supply can only deliver 15 amperes, the output voltage will *sag* during the period the key is held down. This reduced or unregulated voltage may affect the frequency-determining circuit. If so, the transmitter may shift frequency slightly and the received signal will have a chirping sound to it. The cure is to have an adequately rated regulated-voltage power supply connected to the transmitter. (N8A09)

Power supplies can cause another problem on both the CW and voice modes. If the power supply has a defective or inadequate electrolytic filter capacitor it may allow some of the AC power to be impressed on the DC power output. In this case, the DC power is said to be inadequately filtered. Inadequate filtering can cause a hum or buzzing sound to be superimposed on the transmitted signal. The cure is to either repair or replace the power supply. (N8A10)

Spurious Emissions

Spurious emissions are created when a transmitter radiates signals outside the Amateur band during transmissions. One form of spurious signal is the harmonic. (N8B05)

Harmonics—What is a harmonic? It is defined as the *multiple of a fundamental frequency*. The harmonic is considered to be a spurious or unwanted emission. As an example, the fourth harmonic of an emission at 7160 KHz is 28,640 KHz. The second harmonic of a 222 MHz signal is 444 MHz. (N8B01)(N8B02)

Harmonic radiation was quite common with vacuum tube powered equipment, since manual tuning adjustments were used to "tweak" the amplifier circuits. It was not at all unusual to have the amplifier misadjusted to a harmonic, rather than correctly tuned to the fundamental frequency. At one time this was less of a problem since all the high frequency (HF) Amateur bands were harmonically related. The bands were 1.8, 3.5, 7, 14, 21 and 28 MHz. Thus, if your 7 Mhz transmitter radiated a strong second or third harmonic signal, it would still fall in a ham band and not cause trouble to other services.

On the other hand, harmonic emission is more serious today with the various classes of operation in use. For example, let's say a Novice or Tech-Plus station operating on 7,125 KHz radiates an excessive third harmonic on 21,375 KHz. The Novice is legally permitted to operate on the 7 Mhz frequency, but not in that portion of the 21

MHz band. The excessive harmonic signals will be noticed by an FCC monitoring station and a citation will result. (N8B03)

Modern solid-state equipment seldom generate harmonics since there are no adjustments in the high power circuit, such as for vacuum tube rigs. Harmonics are eliminated by **low pass filters.**

Incidentally, spurious emissions don't always radiate from your antenna system. If you were to operate a transmitter or high power linear amplifier with the covers and shields removed, the internal circuitry can directly radiate spurious emissions which interfere with nearby television sets. The direct radiation energy bypasses and avoids the spurious emission elimination filters. (N8B06)

Splatter—Turning up the microphone gain on a transmitter, or shouting into the microphone, can cause a problem called **overmodulation**. In an FM radio, such as a hand held, the overmodulation is called **overdeviation**. Overmodulation can cause a transmitted voice to spread out or *splatter* and interfere with stations operating on nearby channels. The same effect can occur if you turn on *speech processing* circuits when the microphone volume is too high. If someone told you that signals from your handheld transceiver were interfering with other signals on a frequency near yours, your hand held might be transmitting spurious signals such as splatter. (N8B04)(N8B07) (N8B08)(N8B09)(N8B09)(N8B11)(T8B10)(T8B11)

With this background, see how you do answering the following questions.

Novice Subelement 8 (2 questions)

N8A01—How is CW usually transmitted? (A) By frequency-shift keying an RF signal; (B) By on/off keying an RF signal; (C) By audio-frequency-shift keying an oscillator tone; (D) By on/off keying an audio-frequency signal.

N8A02—How is RTTY usually transmitted? (A) By frequency-shift keying an RF signal; (B) By on/off keying an RF signal; (C) By digital pulse-code keying of an unmodulated carrier; (D) By on/off keying an audio-frequency signal.

N8A03—What is the name for international Morse code emissions? (A) RTTY; (B) Data; (C) CW; (D) Phone.

N8A04—What is the name for narrow-band direct-printing telegraphy emissions? (A) RTTY; (B) Data; (C) CW; (D) Phone.

N8A05—What is the name for packet-radio emissions? (A) RTTY; (B) Data; (C) CW; (D) Phone.

N8A06—What is the name for voice emissions? (A) RTTY; (B) Data; (C) CW; (D) Phone.

N8A07—How can you prevent key clicks? (A) By sending CW more slowly; (B) By increasing power; (C) By using a better power supply; (D) By using a key-click filter.

N8A08—What does chirp mean? (A) An overload in a receiver's audio circuit whenever CW is received; (B) A high-pitched tone which is received along with a CW signal; (C) A small change in a transmitter's frequency each time it is keyed; (D) A slow change in transmitter frequency as the circuit warms up.

N8A09—What can be done to keep a CW transmitter from chirping? (A) Add a low-pass filter; (B) Use an RF amplifier; (C) Keep the power supply current very steady; (D) Keep the power supply voltages very steady.

N8A10—What may cause a buzzing or hum in the signal of an HF transmitter? (A) Using an antenna which is the wrong length; (B) Energy from another transmitter; (C) Bad design of the transmitter's RF power output circuit; (D) A bad filter capacitor in the transmitter's power supply.

N8A11—Which sideband is commonly used for 10-meter phone operation? (A) Uppper-sideband; (B) Lower-sideband; (C) Amplitude-compandored sideband; (D) Double-sideband.

N8B01—How does the frequency of a harmonic compare to the desired transmitting frequency? (A) It is slightly more than the desired frequency; (B) It is slightly less than the desired frequency; (C) It is exactly two, or three, or more times the desired frequency; (D) It is much less than the desired frequency.

N8B02—What is the fourth harmonic of a 7160-kHz signal? (A) 28,640 kHz; (B) 35,800 kHz; (C) 28,160 kHz; (D) 1790 kHz.

N8B03—If you are told your station was heard on 21,375 kHz, but at the time you were operating on 7125 kHz, what is one reason this could happen? (A) Your transmitter's power-supply filter capacitor was bad; (B) You were sending CW too fast; (C) Your transmitter was radiating harmonic signals; (D) Your transmitter's power-supply filter choke was bad.

N8B04—If someone tells you that signals from your hand held transceiver are interfering with other signals on a frequency near yours, what may be the cause? (A) You may need a power amplifier for your hand held; (B) Your hand held may have chirp from weak batteries; (C) You may need to turn the volume up on your hand held; (D) Your hand held may be transmitting spurious emissions.

N8B05—If your transmitter sends signals outside the band where it is transmitting, what is this called? (A) Off-frequency emissions; (B) Transmitter chirping; (C) Side tones; (D) Spurious emissions.

N8B06—What problem may occur if your transmitter is operated without the cover and other shielding in place? (A) It may transmit spurious emissions; (B) It may transmit a chirpy signal; (C) It may transmit a weak signal; (D) It may interfere with other stations operating near its frequency.

N8B07—What may happen if an SSB transmitter is operated with the microphone gain set too high? (A) It may cause digital interference to computer equipment; (B) It may cause splatter interference to other stations operating near its frequency; (C) It may cause atmospheric interference in the air around the antenna; (D) It may cause interference to other stations operating on a higher frequency band.

N8B08—What may happen if an SSB transmitter is operated with too much speech processing? (A) It may cause digital interference to computer equipment; (B) It may cause splatter interference to other stations operating near its frequency; (C) It may cause atmospheric interference in the air around the antenna; (D) It may cause interference to other stations operating on a higher frequency band.

N8B09—What may happen if an FM transmitter is operated with the microphone gain or deviation control set too high? (A) It may cause digital interference to computer equipment; (B) It may cause interference to other stations operating near its frequency; (C) It may cause atmospheric interference in the air around the antenna; (D) It may cause interference to other stations operating on a higher frequency band.

N8B10—What may your FM hand held or mobile transceiver do if you shout into its microphone? (A) It may cause digital interference to computer equipment; (B) It may cause interference to other stations operating near its frequency; (C) It may cause atmospheric interference in the air around the antenna; (D) It may cause interference to other stations operating on a higher frequency band.

N8B11—What can you do if you are told your FM hand held or mobile transceiver is over deviating? (A) Talk louder into the microphone; (B) Let the transceiver cool off; (C) Change to a higher power level; (D) Talk further away from the microphone

Technician Subelement 8 (2 questions)

T8A01—What is the name for unmodulated carrier wave emissions? (A) Phone; (B) Test; (C) CW; (D) RTTY.

T8A02—What is the name for Morse code emissions produced by switching a transmitter's output on and off? (A) Phone; (B) Test; (C) CW; (D) RTTY.

T8A03—What is RTTY? (A) Amplitude-keyed telegraphy; (B) Frequency-shift-keyed telegraphy; (C) Frequency-modulated telephony; (D) Phase-modulated telephony.

T8A04—What is the name for packet-radio emissions? (A) CW; (B) Data; (C) Phone; (D) RTTY.

T8A05—How is tone-modulated Morse code produced? (A) By feeding a microphone's audio signal into an FM transmitter; (B) By feeding an on/off keyed audio tone into a CW transmitter; (C) By on/off keying of a carrier; (D) By feeding an on/off keyed audio tone into a transmitter.

T8A06—What is the name of the voice emission most used on VHF/UHF repeaters? (A) Single-sideband phone; (B) Pulse-modulated phone; (C) Slow-scan phone; (D) Frequency modulated phone.

T8A07—What is the name of the voice emission most used on Amateur HF bands? (A) Single-sideband phone; (B) Pulse-modulated phone; (C) Slow-scan phone; (D) Frequency modulated phone.

T8A08—What is meant by the upper-sideband (USB)? (A) The part of a single-sideband signal which is above the carrier frequency; (B) The part of a single-sideband signal which is below the carrier frequency; (C) Any frequency above 10 MHz; (D) The carrier frequency of a single-sideband signal.

T8A09—What emissions are produced by a transmitter using a reactance modulator? (A) CW; (B) Test; (C) Single-sideband, suppressed-carrier phone; (D) Phase-modulated phone.

T8A10—What other emission does phase modulation most resemble? (A) Amplitude modulation; (B) Pulse modulation; (C) Frequency modulation; (D) Single-sideband modulation.

T8A11—What is the name for emissions produced by an on/off keyed audio tone? (A) RTTY; (B) MCW; (C) CW; (D) Phone.

T8B01—What is another name for a constant-amplitude radio-frequency signal? (A) An RF carrier; (B) An AF carrier; (C) A sideband carrier; (D) A subcarrier.

T8B02—What is modulation? (A) Varying a radio wave in some way to send information; (B) Receiving audio information from a signal; (C) Increasing the power of a transmitter; (D) Suppressing the carrier in a single-sideband transmitter.

T8B03—What kind of emission would your FM transmitter produce if its microphone failed to work? (A) An unmodulated carrier; (B) A phase-modulated carrier; (C) An amplitude-modulated carrier; (D) A frequency-modulated carrier.

T8B04—How would you modulate a 2-meter FM transceiver to produce packet-radio emissions? (A) Connect a terminal-node-controller to interrupt the transceiver's carrier wave; (B) Connect a terminal-node-controller to the transceiver's microphone input; (C) Connect a keyboard to the transceiver's microphone input; (D) Connect a DTMF key pad to the transceiver's microphone input.

T8B05—Why is FM voice best for local VHF/UHF radio communications? (A) The carrier is not detectable; (B) It is more resistant to distortion caused by reflected signals; (C) It has high-fidelity audio which can be understood even when the signal is somewhat weak; (D) Its RF carrier stays on frequency better than the AM modes.

T8B06—Why do many radio receivers have several IF filters of different bandwidths that can be selected by the operator? (A) Because some frequency bands are wider than others; (B) Because different bandwidths help increase the receiver sensitivity; (C) Because different bandwidths improve S-meter readings; (D) Because some emission types need a wider bandwidth than others to be received properly.

T8B07—Which list of emission types is in order from the narrowest bandwidth to the widest bandwidth? (A) RTTY, CW, SSB voice, FM voice; (B) CW, FM voice, RTTY, SSB voice; (C) CW, RTTY, SSB voice, FM voice; (D) CW, SSB voice, RTTY, FM voice.

T8B08—What is the usual bandwidth of a single-sideband Amateur signal? (A) 1 kHz; (B) 2 kHz; (C) Between 3 and 6 kHz; (D) Between 2 and 3 kHz.

T8B09—What is the usual bandwidth of a frequency-modulated Amateur signal? (A) Less than 5 kHz; (B) Between 5 and 10 kHz; (C) Between 10 and 20 kHz; (D) Greater than 20 kHz.

T8B10—What is the result of overdeviation in an FM transmitter? (A) Increased transmitter power; (B) Out-of-channel emissions; (C) Increased transmitter range; (D) Poor carrier suppression.

T8B11—What causes splatter interference? (A) Keying a transmitter too fast; (B) Signals from a transmitter's output circuit are being sent back to its input circuit; (C) Overmodulation of a transmitter; (D) The transmitting antenna is the wrong length.

Chapter

9

Antennas and Feedlines

This final section of the Technician test will present three questions each from Element 2 and 3A.

Antennas are one of the most fascinating subjects in the field of Amateur radio. Amateurs have many opinions as to the relative merits of various types of antenna. Some claim the **beam** is better while others swear by the **cubical quad**. Some rugged individualists insist that a single **vertical** is best of all for working distant stations.

Amateur Radio Antennas

An Amateur antenna need not be complicated. It can be as simple as stringing up a random length of wire such as that shown in *Figure 9-1*. For transmitting, a random length antenna must be used with an impedance matching device. More about that later.

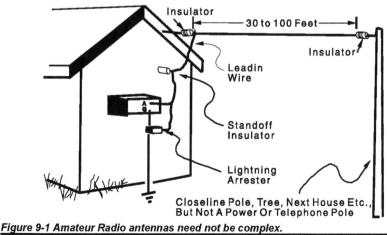

Figure 9-1 Amateur Radio antennas need not be complex.

Antennas come in all shapes and sizes. A number of years ago, it was popular to design vertical antennas using soda cans soldered together. The operating frequency was designed by varying the number of cans used in order to make *the correct length*. Unfortunately, with aluminum cans, this is no longer a practical way to make a vertical antenna.

Resonant Frequency

The correct length? Yes—the length of an antenna is crucially important to it's performance. As you might expect, reducing the length reduces the antenna performance. Surprisingly, the same thing happens if you increase the length of the antenna! There is a critical length where the antenna works the best. *Maximum voltage is induced in the antenna when the length of the antenna is the same as the wavelength of the radio signal reaching it.* This is called the **resonant frequency** of the antenna.

The simplest and best performing antenna is called the **half-wave dipole**. The length, from tip-to-tip, is approximately one-half the wavelength of a specific frequency. Imagine for a moment that you could tape measure the distance between the peaks and valleys of a radio frequency signal. If you measured from one positive peak to an adjacent positive peak, the distance would be the wavelength for that frequency. The distance from a positive peak to a negative peak (or the other way around) would be a half wavelength.

Antenna Directivity

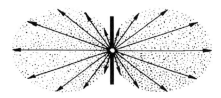

The dipole has a directive characteristic. *Figure 9-2* shows the radiation (and reception sensitivity) characteristics of a dipole antenna looking down on it from above. Note that the signal (and reception sensitivity) is maximum broadside to the dipole element. In other words, if the antenna points east and west, the direction of maximum radiation would be north and south. (N9B09)

Figure 9-2 A dipole is directional broadside to its length with very low pickup from the ends. Arrows indicate the sensitivity in a given direction.

There is a very deep null off the ends of the antenna. This, by the way, is the basis for direction finding equipment. The dipole is rotated until the null is indicated. The end of the dipole points in the direction of the station you are trying to locate by direction finding.

You can also see that if the dipole is positioned vertically it will *radiate equally well in all directions*. There will still be a null above the antenna. The null below the antenna doesn't matter, since a vertical antenna is usually a quarter wave and is mounted on the ground or a car top. The conductive surface the antenna is mounted on provides the other quarter wave to make up the optimum quarter wavelength. (N9B08)

Single Element Antennas

How do we know how long to make the antenna for a specific frequency? We use a "magic number" called a **constant**. In the case of a half-wave dipole antenna, the "magic number" is **468**. Remember that number—it's important and you will almost certainly be asked a test question related to antenna length.

Half Wave—You can determine the length of the half-wave dipole by dividing the desired frequency (in megaHertz) into 468 (468/f). Say you want to calculate the length of a dipole for 3,725 kHz in the 80 meter Novice band. First, we must convert kiloHertz to megaHertz. As I'm sure you remember from *Chapter 5*, 3,725 kHz is the same as 3.725 MHz. Divide that number into 468. The answer is that a dipole for 3.7 MHz is 126 feet, rounded off to the nearest foot. To see if you have the idea, what is the length of a half-wavelength dipole for 28.150 MHz? (N9A01)(N9A03)(N9A04)

Incidentally, determining the answer to this sort of test question will be much easier if you have a calculator. You are permitted to bring a calculator to your testing session.

Polarization—Most dipoles are mounted so that they are *parallel* to the surface of the earth. Such an antenna (or antenna element) is said to be *horizontally polarized*. This means that the electromagnetic-wave lines of force are radiated parallel to the earth's surface. If a dipole is mounted so that it is *perpendicular* to the earth's surface, the antenna (or antenna element) will radiate electromagnetic line-of-force that are *vertically polarized* with respect to the surface of the earth. An illustration of antenna polarization is shown in *Figure 9-3*. (T9B01)(T9B02)

Vertical polarization is the polarity most commonly used in VHF work, since many of the stations are mobile. Automobiles do not lend themselves to the installation of horizontally polarized antenna systems. This is somewhat unfortunate, since most man-made electrical *noise and interference is also vertically polarized*. There would be some interference rejection on VHF if it were of the opposite polarization. (T9B05)

Quarter Wave—How do you calculate the length of a quarter-wave antenna such as a vertical that you might install on your car? Easy. Simply calculate it as a half-wave dipole as described above and then divide by two. Thus, if you were making a quarter wave vertical for 7,125 kHz out of soda cans, how tall would it be? Divide 468 by 7.125 and the answer is 66.7 feet. Divide by two to arrive at the answer of approximately 34 feet, rounded to the nearest foot. Got the idea? Ok, what would the length of a quarter wave antenna be for 21.125 MHz? (N9A05)(N9A06)

From the formula you can see that as the frequency is *lowered*, the antenna becomes *longer*. By the same token, if an antenna length is *shortened*, it's resonant frequency *increases*. If the antenna is lengthened or shortened, the resonant frequency is decreased or increased respectively. (N9A08)(N9A09)(N9A10)(N9A11)

The formula is also used at VHF. However, at these frequencies, even inches are important. For this reason, we should not round off numbers as we did for the longer, low-frequency antennas. You can convert the 468 constant from feet to inches by multiplying 12 (inches in one foot) and 468. The new "inches constant" becomes 5616 rather than 468. To calculate the length of a half-wave vertical antenna for 223 MHz in inches, try this. Divide 223 into 5616. The answer, to the nearest inch, is 25. (N9A07)

Now, if you like, you can measure a soda can and see how many it will require to make the antenna. This question is not on your test, however! But, always read a test question carefully to see if the length for a quarter or half wave antenna is required and if the frequency is in kHz or MHz. The formula, once again is 468 divided by the frequency in MHz (468/f). (N9A02)

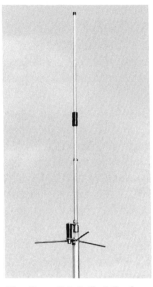

The three "stubs" at the base provide the ground plane for the AR-270 antenna.

The Ground Plane— The ground-plane antenna is considered to be a quarter-wave vertically polarized antenna. Essentially a quarter-wave radiator is used in conjunction with a conducting plane which provides the "other half" of the dipole antenna. The conducting plane can be the earth itself (poor), wires buried in the earth (better) or the roof of an automobile (best). The ground plane is very popular due to its simplicity, excellent performance and the fact that it may be easily constructed by newcomers at home. (T9A09)

When a vertical "whip" is mounted on a vehicle (either by drilling a hole in the roof or with a magnetic mount), the antenna is considered to be a ground plane. This type of antenna, like other forms of vertical antennas, is characterized by the fact that vertical element radiates equally in all directions. (T9A10) (T9A11)

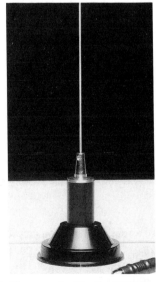

5/8th Wave Antenna—So far we have spoken of half- and quarter-wave antennas. With special designs, it is possible to make antennas which are resonant and radiate properly, but are not a multiple of a quarter wavelength. A 5/8 wave antenna *radiates a stronger signal* than a 1/4 wave and is said to have somewhat more gain over a quarter wave reference. This type of antenna is also favored because it has a lower angle of radiation. In other words, like the vertical antenna discussed above, the 5/8 wavelength antenna radiates

The popular Hustler FX-2 is a good example of a 5/8 wave antenna.

This photo shows a typical Amateur Radio beam antenna used for HF communication.

equally in all compass directions, with most of the radiation going close to the horizon. For this reason, the 5/8 wavelength antenna is very popular for mobile installations. (N9B07)

This may be confusing since it was stated earlier that an antenna works best when it is a multiple of a quarter wave. By using special networks at the base, it is possible to make an antenna (other than a quarter-or half-wavelength) which is extremely efficient. The network is sometimes contained in a little plastic "blob" located at the base of the antenna.

The Beam Antenna

The radiation pattern of an antenna can be modified by placing other element(s) near the radiator. This technique has been used for years in broadcasting to squirt the radio station's signal in a given direction. For example, consider a radio station broadcasting in Santa Barbara, California. The major listening audience is not to the west of the station. That's the Pacific Ocean. By adding additional elements to their antenna system, the "wasted" energy to the west can be redirected toward the land.

Strictly speaking, an antenna which redirects the beam of a normally non-directional radiator is called a **beam antenna**. It produces a radiation pattern with most of the transmitted signal concentrated in a particular direction and attenuated in other directions. (T9A01)

The Yagi Antenna—When the term "beam" is mentioned, an Amateur usually thinks of a series of parallel rods fastened to a central support called a *boom*. In actual fact, this describes beam antenna for concentrating radiation in one direction, called a **Yagi**. Since the added parallel rods receive their radio frequency energy by inductor

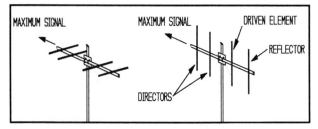

MAXIMUM SIGNAL

MAXIMUM SIGNAL

DRIVEN ELEMENT

REFLECTOR

DIRECTORS

Figure 9-3 The polarity of the radiated wave from a Yagi antenna is determined by which way the antenna is mounted. The antenna shown is a four-element Yagi with two directors.

or radiation from a driven element, the Yagi is referred to as a parasitic beam antenna. (T9A05)

The Yagi is actually a series of formulas, developed by a Japanese engineer, Dr. Yagi, which describes the optimum spacing and length of the elements of this type of beam antenna.

He started with a half-wavelength dipole. This is referred to as the *directly driven element* in a Yagi antenna. Usually a Yagi has only one driven element. The good Dr. found that if an undriven element (a metal rod or wire) was placed parallel to the driven element and made about 5% longer, it would reflect or redirect the radiation. This parasitic element is called the *reflector*. He further found that another element placed forward of the radiating element and made 5% shorter, would reinforce the forward strength of the radiation. This parasitic element is called the *director*. (N9B02)(N9B03) (N9B04)(N9B05)(T9A02)(T9A03)(T9A04)(T9A06)

The accompanying photo shows the construction of a simple parasitic beam Yagi antenna. Note that the relative lengths of the elements are exaggerated to show that the reflector (1) is longer and the director (3) is shorter than the radiating element (2). If you imagine that it is an arrow head, *the direction of maximum radiation* is from the "point" at the left side of the drawing. (N9B01) (N9B06)

As more and more directors are added to the Yagi antenna, the radiation that is normally lost to the side of the antenna is redirected to the forward radiation **lobe**. As directors are added, the antenna is said to be more **directive**.

If the beam or Yagi antenna is mounted with its elements parallel to the earth, the antenna is said to be horizontally polarized. If the antenna is perpendicular with respect to the ground, it radiates a vertically polar-

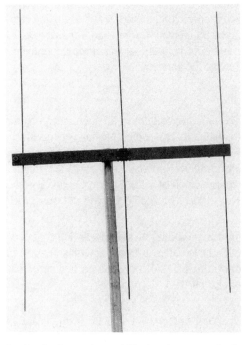

A simple three-element Yagi antenna made for commercial service.

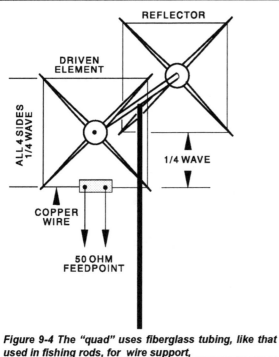

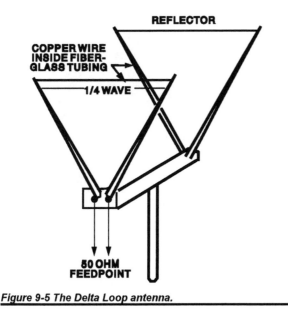

ized wave. A Yagi with vertical or horizontal polarization is illustrated in *Figure 9-3.* (T9B03) (T9B04)

The Cubical Quad—One of the favorite antennas among Amateurs is the **cubical quad**. You can easily recognize one when driving through a neighborhood. The antenna uses two or more x-shaped spreaders with a wire stretched between the four tips in a cube shape. Each side of the wire cube is approximately one quarter wavelength (actually 251/F) long. Thus the total wire length of each loop is approximately one wavelength at the design frequency. (T9A07)

Figure 9-4 The "quad" uses fiberglass tubing, like that used in fishing rods, for wire support,

The driven array is mounted at one end of a boom. At the other end is a similar looking structure. This is the parasitic element which usually functions like the reflector in the Yagi-type antenna. The construction of a typical cubical quad is shown in *Figure 9-4*. There may be more parasitic elements on a huge quad but the majority employ a driven element and a reflector. Some quads have as many as three wire loops on each array. These are quads which operate on more than one band.

The Delta Loop—The Delta Loop antenna (*Figure 9-5*) is similar to the Quad, but has only three sides like a triangle. Each side of the triangle is a *quarter wavelength*. A special matching network is required to feed the delta loop with coax cable. In theory, the antenna should not perform quite as well as the quad, but it has a number of supporters of its performance. (T9A08)

Figure 9-5 The Delta Loop antenna.

Standing Wave Ratio (SWR)

Once again the subject of *standing waves* rears it electromagnetic head in our discussions. Standing waves on a transmission or feed line (see next section) result when there is an impedance mismatch, usually between the antenna and the line. The term ratio describes the level of the maximum to minimum voltage on the transmission line. You should use an impedance matching device whenever the impedance of the cable does not equal the impedance of the antenna. (N9C09)(T9B06)

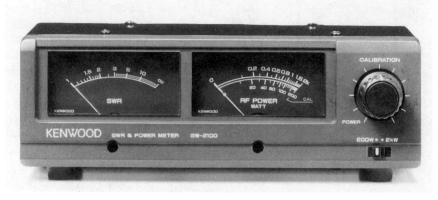

The Kenwood Model SW-2100 features both SWR and power measurement. The right meter measures 200 watts and 2 kilowatts full scale.

Let's see if we can acutally visualize in our minds what happens. I'm going to feed one watt of RF into a piece of 50 ohm coax. This is called the *forward power*. At the other end I've connected a 50 ohm, 2 watt carbon composition resistor. The resistor represents the termination resistance of a perfect antenna. In this example, the output impedance of the transmitter matches that of the transmission line and the line, in

The Diamond SX-600 is unique in that it features HF, VHF and UHF sensors, plus three power scales.

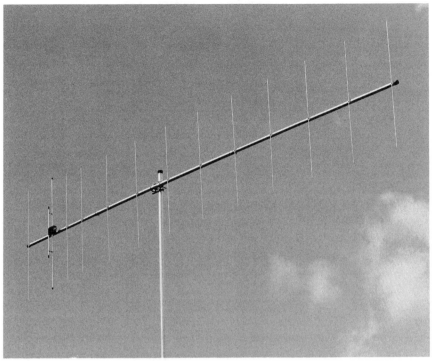

This Yagi antenna feature 13 elements and has a forward gain in excess of 15 dB.

turn, matches the impedance of the "antenna" (the resistor). If I could connect a meter on the center conductor inside the coax, we would find the meter measures 7 volts *at any point along its length.* This shows there are no standing waves. (T9B07)

Now, I'm going to replace the 50 ohm resistor with one measuring 100 ohms. Now, the "antenna" no longer matches the impedance of the tranmission line. It is said to be mismatched. As a result, it will no longer absorb all the power sent to it via the transmission line. Some of the power will be reflected back toward the transmitter. This is said to be the *reflected power.* (T9B08)

When standing waves are present on the transmission line, the reflected radio frequency voltage will *add to and subtract* from the forward radio frequency voltage. Thus, if we measure the voltage along the length of the transmission line as before, it will now measure *above and below 7 volts* at various points along the cable. This indicates the presence of standing waves.

The standing waves will confuse the reading of a directional wattmeter. This instrument measures the power in the forward and reverse (or reflected) direction. The standing waves also cause power to be lost. The loss will increase with increasing SWR. This *lost power is dissipated as heat* in the coax cable, transmitter and even the antenna. If a high-power radio frequency amplifier is feeding a coax line with high SWR, it is not unusual to actually feel heat when you grasp the cable! (T9B09)(T9C08)

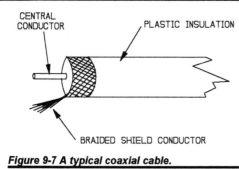

CENTRAL CONDUCTOR
PLASTIC INSULATION
BRAIDED SHIELD CONDUCTOR

Figure 9-7 A typical coaxial cable.

Transmission Lines

With the exception of hand-held transceivers, antennas are seldom located near the Amateur radio station equipment. Usually, it is necessary to route the radio frequency from the transmitter to the antenna and the energy intercepted by the antenna to the receiver. The medium to accomplish this is called the **transmission line**.

Coaxial Cable—The most popular form of transmission line is called **coaxial cable**. It is characterized as round and is usually covered with black plastic weatherproof insulation, as shown in *Figure 9-7*. Inside the coax cable, there is a central conductor, either solid or stranded. This is surrounded by a high quality, high frequency insulation, usually polystyrene. On top of this is a braided shield of copper or tin-plated copper wire.

Since it is weatherproof, coaxial cable can be buried in the ground. The advantage of coaxial cable is that all the radiation is carried inside the shielded "pipe." Thus, it is unaffected by nearby metallic objects. It's 50 ohm impedance rating matches that of receiving and transmitting equipment and most Amateur antennas. (N9C01)(N9C02)(N9C03)(N9C04)

Balanced Feeds—So far we have discussed only unbalanced systems using coaxial cable. *Unbalanced* means a transmission line with one conductor carrying the RF energy and the other *connected to ground*. (T9B10)

Twin lead transmission lines are popular when used with an antenna coupler. It will operate with a high SWR, and has less loss than coaxial cable. Twin lead or parallel conductor transmission line has two wires held apart a specific distance by an insulating material. The insulator can be continuous like the chocolate brown television wire, or it can utilize individual insulator or spreaders spaced along the length of the line. This type of transmission line is sometimes called ladder line because of the similarity in appearance to a ladder (see *Figure 9-7*). (N9C05)(N9C06)(N9C08)

There are disadvantages to this type of transmission line. It must be spaced well away from nearby metal objects or they can absorb some of the transmitter power. For example, if the open wire transmission line is run near the telephone wires coming into your home, you might actually hear your voice. It can be strong enough to interfere with the telephone conversation. Another disadvantage is that open wire transmission line must be used with an antenna coupler. (N9C07)

A mismatch situation might occur if one tried to use a 40-meter antenna on the 15 or 20 meter band. It would not be the right length and would exhibit a high **SWR (standing wave ratio)**. An antenna that is not resonant (the wrong length) simply won't

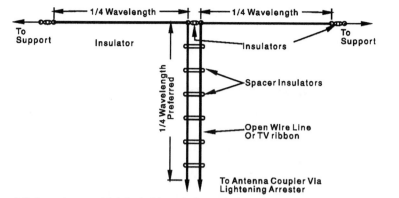

Figure 9-7 An antenna which is fed by a balanced open-wire feedline need not use specific length dipole elements. An antenna coupler can match most lengths of dipole.

work with a coaxial cable transmission line. The open wire lead can be used, however, since it will withstand a much higher SWR than coaxial cable. The antenna coupler can be used to match the high impedance of the antenna to the fixed 50-ohm output impedance of the transmitter and receiver.

A solid dielectric open wire transmission line, such as TV twin-lead, can also be used with the antenna in *Figure 9-8*. This type of transmission line is characterized as two parallel wires held apart at constant spacing by a continuous insulating material (usually polystyrene), rather than individual insulators.

Connectors

It is usually not possible to have one continous length of feed line from the transmitter to the antenna. Amateurs use antenna switches, couplers or other tuning devices and meters in series with this line. Each of these devices uses a connector for its input and/or output point.

A typical connector, used on equipment below 30 MHz, is called an SO-239. The matching plug, which is used on the transmission line, is called a PL-259. How did they get these names? These connectors were designed and implemented during World War II. A connector on equipment was called a socket (SO) and the SO-239 is just one of a series used during that period. The connector mounted on the coax was referred to as a plug (PL) and, again, was one of a series. (T9C01)

The SO-239 and PL-259 connectors exhibit excessive loss and introduce standing waves when used at VHF or UHF. A preferred connector for these bands is known as a type-N connector. (T9C03)

One of the most common connectors, with which most newcomers are familiar, is found on top of virtually every hand-held transceiver. It is called a BNC connector. The whip antenna mounts on the BNC by pushing down and twisting to the right. (T9C02)

Any connector which carries RF energy should be regularly cleaned and tightened to keep its resistance and loss to a minimum. This is also true for the antenna connections. Any resistance which develops (usually due to corrosion) is in series with the path of RF energy which will increase loss and heating. (T9C11)

The SGC, Inc. SG-230 is computer controlled with a half-million circuit combinations! It will match any wire between 8 and 200 foot, with an impedance between 10 ohms and 10 Kohms.

Impedance Matching

Couplers—An antenna coupler is a great matching device when located near the transmitter/receiver. But what about the case where you want to provide a match between a 35-ohm antenna and the 50-ohm transmission line. An impedance matching device is required at the antenna.

Some intelligent, computer-controlled couplers like the SGC, Inc. "Smartuner" can be mounted right at the dipole feed-point. It uses a CPU to calculate the correct tuning adjustments and can retune itself in a fraction of a second.

The Balun—There is another device that provides a limited amount of impedance matching capability between the transmission line and the antenna. More important, it can also be used to connect the *balanced* feed-point of the dipole antenna *to* the *unbalanced* coaxial cable. The device is called a **balun**. This stands for *balanced-to-unbalanced*. (N9C10)(T9B11)

Let's say you want to feed your balanced dipole with unbalanced 50-ohm coaxial cable. You could make a perfect match by connecting a balun at the antenna. (N9C11)

The balun can also be used at the transmitter/receiver end of the transmission line. Consider the case where you want to connect an open wire 200-ohm parallel conductor line to your transmitter receiver. It can be connected between the parallel wire transmission line and the 50 ohm unbalanced output of your equipment.

The dipole and quad mentioned earlier are balanced antenna systems. This means the antenna (or driven element in a beam) is balanced or equal on each side of the feed point.

A whip antenna on the roof of an automobile is certainly not balanced. The wire whip is one-half of the dipole, while the metal roof replaces the other half. This is an unbalanced antenna and is always fed with coax. An unbalanced antenna (or driven element in an array) is not symmetrical or identical on each side of the feed point.

A balanced line is one in which neither conductor is connected to ground. An example of a balanced line is the television cable mentioned earlier.

The MFJ Noise Bridge can be used to adjust an antenna for optimum performance.

Some Amateurs claim that the signal pattern of an antenna is skewed to one side when an unbalanced coax is used to drive a balanced antenna. A balun can be used to correct the situation, if desired.

Cable Loss—As we know all too well, nothing is perfect in this world. The adage certainly holds true for transmission lines carrying radio frequency energy. If we drive one end of a coax with one watt of RF, something less than one watt will emerge from the other end due to *inherent loss in any transmission line*. The *longer the line,* and/or *the higher the frequency* of the radio frequency energy, *the greater the loss*. Since the loss is always present, one should cut off any excess cable to make it as short and direct as possible. (T9C05)(T9C06)(T9C07)

Open wire line will have less loss than coaxial cable below 30 MHz. As a general rule, cable loss is proportional to size. RG-8 is about 5/8" in diameter and some of the special foam dielectric versions, such as *RG-213*, have *exceptionally low loss*. It is the preferred cable for long runs. RG-58 is about the diameter of a pencil and has noticeably more loss per 100 feet. The smallest common coax is RG-174 (about the size of a soda straw) has even more loss. From the preceding explanation you can see that for feeding long runs to a VHF antenna, you would select RG-213 coax for the lowest loss characteristic. (T9C04)

Cable loss is proportional to length and frequency. The longer the run and the higher the frequency, the greater the loss. To minimize loss, you should cut off any excess cable after it had been routed from the antenna to the ham station.

Antenna Radiation and Safety

Even though it was mentioned in previous chapters, it is not repetitious to mention that radio frequency radiation can be harmful, particularly if it is prolonged and/or a high intensity. Remember, when using a hand-held radio, position the antenna away from your head as far as possible. (N9B10)

If you purchase or upgrade a hand-held radio, you have the choice of antenna styles. It is generally believed that a 1/2 wavelength whip antenna causes the least amount of radiation near the head. The short, helically wound, flexible antennas are the worst, since the energy is concentrated just a few inches above the top of the hand-held.

The precaution is also valid for an antenna that you erect. It should be high and out-of-reach. This will prevent anyone from touching the antenna and getting an RF burn or receiving excessive exposure to RF radiation. Observe the same precaution with parallel transmission lines, since they also have dangerously high RF voltage on the exposed open wires. (N9B11)(T9C09)(T9C10)

Now let's tackle the questions on antennas and transmission lines associated with this final chapter.

Novice Subelement 9 (3 questions)

N9A01—How do you calculate the length (in feet) of a half-wavelength dipole antenna? (A) Divide 150 by the antenna's operating frequency (in MHz) [150/f(in MHz)]; (B) Divide 234 by the antenna's operating frequency (in MHz) [234/f (in MHz)]; (C) Divide 300 by the antenna's operating frequency (in MHz) [300/f (in MHz)]; (D) Divide 468 by the antenna's operating frequency (in MHz) [468/f (in MHz)]

N9A02—How do you calculate the length (in feet) of a quarter-wavelength vertical antenna? (A) Divide 150 by the antenna's operating frequency (in MHz) [150/f (in MHz)]; (B) Divide 234 by the antenna's operating frequency (in MHz) [234/f (in MHz)]; (C) Divide 300 by the antenna's operating frequency (in MHz) [300/f (in MHz)]; (D) Divide 468 by the antenna's operating frequency (in MHz) [468/f (in MHz)]

N9A03—If you made a half-wavelength dipole antenna for 3725 kHz, how long would it be (to the nearest foot)? (A) 126 ft; (B) 81 ft; (C) 63 ft; (D) 40 ft

N9A04—If you made a half-wavelength dipole antenna for 28.150 MHz, how long would it be (to the nearest foot)? (A) 22 ft; (B) 11 ft; (C) 17 ft; (D) 34 ft

N9A05—If you made a quarter-wavelength vertical antenna for 7125 kHz, how long would it be (to the nearest foot)? (A) 11 ft; (B) 16 ft; (C) 21 ft; (D) 33 ft

N9A06—If you made a quarter-wavelength vertical antenna for 21.125 MHz, how long would it be (to the nearest foot)? (A) 7 ft; (B) 11 ft; (C) 14 ft; (D) 22 ft

N9A07—If you made a half-wavelength vertical antenna for 223 MHz, how long would it be (to the nearest inch)? (A) 112 inches; (B) 50 inches; (C) 25 inches; (D) 12 inches

N9A08—If an antenna is made longer, what happens to its resonant frequency? (A) It decreases; (B) It increases; (C) It stays the same; (D) It disappears

N9A09—If an antenna is made shorter, what happens to its resonant frequency? (A) It decreases; (B) It increases; (C) It stays the same; (D) It disappears

N9A10—How could you lower the resonant frequency of a dipole antenna? (A) Lengthen the antenna; (B) Shorten the antenna; (C) Use less feed line; (D) Use a smaller size feed line

N9A11—How could you raise the resonant frequency of a dipole antenna? (A) Lengthen the antenna; (B) Shorten the antenna; (C) Use more feed line; (D) Use a larger size feed line

N9B01—In what direction does a Yagi antenna send out radio energy? (A) It goes out equally in all directions; (B) Most of it goes in one direction; (C) Most of it goes equally in two opposite directions; (D) Most of it is aimed high into the air

N9B02—About how long is the driven element of a Yagi antenna? (A) 1/4 wavelength; (B) 1/3 wavelength; (C) 1/2 wavelength; (D) 1 wavelength

N9B03—In Diagram N9-1, what is the name of element 2 of the Yagi antenna? (A) Director; (B) Reflector; (C) Boom; (D) Driven element

N9B04—In Diagram N9-1, what is the name of element 3 of the Yagi antenna? (A) Director; (B) Reflector; (C) Boom; (D) Driven element

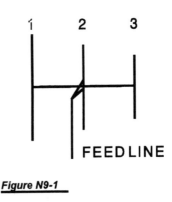
Figure N9-1

N9B05—In Diagram N9-1, what is the name of element 1 of the Yagi antenna? (A) Director; (B) Reflector; (C) Boom; (D) Driven element

N9B06—Looking at the Yagi antenna in Diagram N9-1, in which direction on the page would it send most of its radio energy? (A) Left; (B) Right; (C) Top; (D) Bottom

N9B07—Why is a 5/8-wavelength vertical antenna better than a 1/4-wavelength vertical antenna for VHF or UHF mobile operations? (A) A 5/8-wavelength antenna can handle more power; (B) A 5/8-wavelength antenna has more gain; (C) A 5/8-wavelength antenna has less corona loss; (D) A 5/8-wavelength antenna is easier to install on a car

N9B08—In what direction does a vertical antenna send out radio energy? (A) Most of it goes in two opposite directions; (B) Most of it goes high into the air; (C) Most of it goes equally in all horizontal directions; (D) Most of it goes in one direction

N9B09—If the ends of a half-wave dipole antenna point east and west, which way would the antenna send out radio energy? (A) Equally in all directions; (B) Mostly up and down; (C) Mostly north and south; (D) Mostly east and west

N9B10—How should you hold the antenna of a hand held transceiver while you are transmitting? (A) Away from your head and away from others; (B) Pointed towards the station you are contacting; (C) Pointed away from the station you are contacting; (D) Pointed down to bounce the signal off the ground

N9B11—Why should your outside antennas be high enough so that no one can touch them while you are transmitting? (A) Touching the antenna might cause television interference; (B) Touching the antenna might cause RF burns; (C) Touching the antenna might radiate harmonics; (D) Touching the antenna might reflect the signal back to the transmitter and cause damage

N9C01—What is a coaxial cable? (A) Two wires side-by-side in a plastic ribbon; (B) Two wires side-by-side held apart by insulating rods; (C) Two wires twisted around each other in a spiral; (D) A center wire inside an insulating material covered by a metal sleeve or shield

N9C02—Why does coaxial cable make a good antenna feed line? (A) You can make it at home, and its impedance matches most Amateur antennas; (B) It is weatherproof, and its impedance matches most Amateur antennas; (C) It is weatherproof, and its impedance is higher than that of most Amateur antennas; (D) It can be used near metal objects, and its impedance is higher than that of most Amateur antennas

N9C03—Which kind of antenna feed line can carry radio energy very well even if it is buried in the ground? (A) Twin lead; (B) Coaxial cable; (C) Parallel conductor; (D) Twisted pair

N9C04—What is the best antenna feed line to use if it must be put near grounded metal objects? (A) Coaxial cable; (B) Twin lead; (C) Twisted pair; (D) Ladder-line

N9C05—What is parallel-conductor feed line? (A) Two wires twisted around each other in a spiral; (B) Two wires side-by-side held apart by insulating rods; (C) A center wire inside an insulating material which is covered by a metal sleeve or shield; (D) A metal pipe which is as wide or slightly wider than a wavelength of the signal it carries

N9C06—What are some reasons to use parallel-conductor feed line? (A) It has low impedance, and will operate with a high SWR; (B) It will operate with a high SWR, and it works well when tied down to metal objects; (C) It has a low impedance, and has less loss than coaxial cable; (D) It will operate with a high SWR, and has less loss than coaxial cable

N9C07—What are some reasons not to use parallel-conductor feed line? (A) It does not work well when tied down to metal objects, and you must use an impedance matching device with your transceiver; (B) It is difficult to make at home, and it does not work very well with a high SWR; (C) It does not work well when tied down to metal objects, and it cannot operate under high power; (D) You must use an impedance matching device with your transceiver, and it does not work very well with a high SWR

N9C08—What kind of antenna feed line is made of two conductors held apart by insulated rods? (A) Coaxial cable; (B) Open-conductor ladder line; (C) Twin lead in a plastic ribbon; (D) Twisted pair

N9C09—What would you use to connect a coaxial cable of 50-ohms impedance to an antenna of 35-ohms impedance? (A) A terminating resistor; (B) An SWR meter; (C) An impedance matching device; (D) A low-pass filter

N9C10—What does balun mean? (A) Balanced antenna network; (B) Balanced unloader; (C) Balanced unmodulator; (D) Balanced to unbalanced

N9C11—Where would you install a balun to feed a dipole antenna with 50-ohm coaxial cable? (A) Between the coaxial cable and the antenna; (B) Between the transmitter and the coaxial cable; (C) Between the antenna and the ground; (D) Between the coaxial cable and the ground

Technician Subelement 9 (3 questions)

T9A01—What is a directional antenna? (A) An antenna which sends and receives radio energy equally well in all directions; (B) An antenna that cannot send and receive radio energy by skywave or skip propagation; (C) An antenna which sends and receives radio energy mainly in one direction; (D) An antenna which sends and receives radio energy equally well in two opposite directions.

T9A02—How is a Yagi antenna constructed? (A) Two or more straight, parallel elements are fixed in line with each other; (B) Two or more square or circular loops are fixed in line with each other; (C) Two or more square or circular loops are stacked inside each other; (D) A straight element is fixed in the center of three or more elements which angle toward the ground.

T9A03—What type of beam antenna uses two or more straight elements arranged in line with each other? (A) A delta loop antenna; (B) A quad antenna; (C) A Yagi antenna; (D) A Zepp antenna.

T9A04—How many directly driven elements do most beam antennas have? (A) None; (B) One; (C) Two; (D) Three.

T9A05—What is a parasitic beam antenna? (A) An antenna where some elements obtain their radio energy by induction or radiation from a driven element; (B) An antenna where wave traps are used to magnetically couple the elements; (C) An antenna where all elements are driven by direct connection to the feed line; (D) An antenna where the driven element obtains its radio energy by induction or radiation from director elements.

T9A06—What are the parasitic elements of a Yagi antenna? (A) The driven element and any reflectors; (B) The director and the driven element; (C) Only the reflectors (if any); (D) Any directors or any reflectors.

T9A07—What is a cubical quad antenna? (A) Four straight, parallel elements in line with each other, each approximately 1/2-electrical wavelength long; (B) Two or more parallel four-sided wire loops, each approximately one-electrical wavelength long; (C) A vertical conductor 1/4-electrical wavelength high, fed at the bottom; (D) A center-fed wire 1/2-electrical wavelength long.

T9A08—What is a delta loop antenna? (A) A type of cubical quad antenna, except with triangular elements rather than square; (B) A large copper ring or wire loop, used in direction finding; (C) An antenna system made of three vertical antennas, arranged in a triangular shape; (D) An antenna made from several triangular coils of wire on an insulating form.

T9A09—What type of non-directional antenna is easy to make at home and works well outdoors? (A) A Yagi; (B) A delta loop; (C) A cubical quad; (D) A ground plane.

T9A10—What type of antenna is made when a magnetic-base whip antenna is placed on the roof of a car? (A) A Yagi; (B) A delta loop; (C) A cubical quad; (D) A ground plane.

T9A11—If a magnetic-base whip antenna is placed on the roof of a car, in what direction does it send out radio energy? (A) It goes out equally well in all horizontal directions; (B) Most of it goes in one direction; (C) Most of it goes equally in two opposite directions; (D) Most of it is aimed high into the air.

T9B01—What does horizontal wave polarization mean? (A) The magnetic lines of force of a radio wave are parallel to the

earth's surface; (B) The electric lines of force of a radio wave are parallel to the earth's surface; (C) The electric lines of force of a radio wave are perpendicular to the earth's surface; (D) The electric and magnetic lines of force of a radio wave are perpendicular to the earth's surface.

T9B02—What does vertical wave polarization mean? (A) The electric lines of force of a radio wave are parallel to the earth's surface; (B) The magnetic lines of force of a radio wave are perpendicular to the earth's surface; (C) The electric lines of force of a radio wave are perpendicular to the earth's surface; (D) The electric and magnetic lines of force of a radio wave are parallel to the earth's surface.

T9B03—What electromagnetic-wave polarization does a Yagi antenna have when its elements are parallel to the earth's surface? (A) Circular; (B) Helical; (C) Horizontal; (D) Vertical.

T9B04—What electromagnetic-wave polarization does a half-wavelength antenna have when it is perpendicular to the earth's surface? (A) Circular; (B) Horizontal; (C) Parabolical; (D) Vertical.

T9B05—What electromagnetic-wave polarization does most man-made electrical noise have in the HF and VHF spectrum? (A) Horizontal; (B) Left-hand circular; (C) Right-hand circular; (D) Vertical.

T9B06—What does standing-wave ratio mean? (A) The ratio of maximum to minimum inductances on a feed line; (B) The ratio of maximum to minimum resistances on a feed line; (C) The ratio of maximum to minimum impedances on a feed line; (D) The ratio of maximum to minimum voltages on a feed line.

T9B07—What does forward power mean? (A) The power traveling from the transmitter to the antenna; (B) The power radiated from the top of an antenna system; (C) The power produced during the positive half of an RF cycle; (D) The power used to drive a linear amplifier.

T9B08—What does reflected power mean? (A) The power radiated down to the ground from an antenna; (B) The power returned to a transmitter from an antenna; (C) The power produced during the negative half of an RF cycle; (D) The power returned to an antenna by buildings and trees.

T9B09—What happens to radio energy when it is sent through a poor quality coaxial cable? (A) It causes spurious emissions; (B) It is returned to the transmitter's chassis ground; (C) It is converted to heat in the cable; (D) It causes interference to other stations near the transmitting frequency.

T9B10—What is an unbalanced line? (A) Feed line with neither conductor connected to ground; (B) Feed line with both conductors connected to ground; (C) Feed line with one conductor connected to ground; (D) Feed line with both conductors connected to each other.

T9B11—What device can be installed to feed a balanced antenna with an unbalanced feed line? (A) A balun; (B) A loading coil; (C) A triaxial transformer; (D) A wavetrap.

T9C01—What common connector usually joins RG-213 coaxial cable to an HF transceiver? (A) An F-type cable connector; (B) A PL-259 connector; (C) A banana plug connector; (D) A binding post connector.

T9C02—What common connector usually joins a hand held transceiver to its antenna? (A) A BNC connector; (B) A PL-259 connector; (C) An F-type cable connector; (D) A binding post connector.

T9C03—Which of these common connectors has the lowest loss at UHF? (A) An F-type cable connector; (B) A type-N connector; (C) A BNC connector; (D) A PL-259 connector.

T9C04—If you install a 6-meter Yagi antenna on a tower 150 feet from your transmitter, which of the following feed lines is best? (A) RG-213; (B) RG-58; (C) RG-59; (D) RG-174.

T9C05—If you have a transmitter and an antenna which are 50 feet apart, but are connected by 200 feet of RG-58 coaxial cable, what should be done to reduce feed line loss? (A) Cut off the excess cable so the feed line is an even number of wavelengths long; (B) Cut off the excess cable so the feed line is an odd number of wavelengths long; (C) Cut off the excess cable; (D) Roll the excess cable into a coil which is as small as possible.

T9C06—As the length of a feed line is changed, what happens to signal loss? (A) Signal loss is the same for any length of feed line; (B) Signal loss increases as length increases; (C) Signal loss decreases as length increases; (D) Signal loss is the least when the length is the same as the signal's wavelength.

T9C07—As the frequency of a signal is changed, what happens to signal loss in a feed line? (A) Signal loss is the same for any frequency; (B) Signal loss increases with increasing frequency; (C) Signal loss increases with decreasing frequency; (D) Signal loss is the least when the signal's wavelength is the same as the feed line's length.

T9C08—If your antenna feed line gets hot when you are transmitting, what might this mean? (A) You should transmit using less power; (B) The conductors in the feed line are not insulated very well; (C) The feed line is too long; (D) The SWR may be too high, or the feed line loss may be high.

T9C09—Why should you make sure that no one can touch an open-wire feed line while you are transmitting with it? (A) Because contact might cause a short circuit and damage the transmitter; (B) Because contact might break the feed line; (C) Because contact might cause spurious emissions; (D) Because high-voltage radio energy might burn the person.

T9C10—For RF safety, what is the best thing to do with your transmitting antennas? (A) Use vertical polarization; (B) Use horizontal polarization; (C) Mount the antennas where no one can come near them; (D) Mount the antenna close to the ground.

T9C11—Why should you regularly clean, tighten and re-solder all antenna connectors? (A) To help keep their resistance at a minimum; (B) To keep them looking nice; (C) To keep them from getting stuck in place; (D) To increase their capacitance

Answers

CHAPTER ONE

N1A01 (A) [97]
N1A02 (B) [97]
N1A03 (A) [97]
N1A04 (D) [97]
N1A05 (A) [97.1]
N1A06 (D) [97.1]
N1A07 (B) [97.3a1]
N1A08 (C) [97.3a4]
N1A09 (D) [97.3a5]
N1A10 (C) [97.3a11]
N1A11 (C) [97.513a]
N1B01 (D) [97.5a]
N1B02 (B) [97.5a]
N1B03 (C) [97.5a]
N1B04 (B) [97.5d]
N1B05 (C) [97.5e]
N1B06 (A) [97.5e]
N1B07 (C) [97.7]
N1B08 (D) [97.9a]
N1B09 (A) [97.9]
N1B10 (B) [97.9]
N1B11 (D) [97.501d]
N1C01 (B) [97.301e]
N1C02 (C) [97.301e]
N1C03 (A) [97.301e]
N1C04 (C) [97.301e]
N1C05 (B) [97.301f]
N1C06 (C) [97.301f]
N1C07 (A) [97.301e]
N1C08 (B) [97.301e]
N1C09 (C) [97.301e]
N1C10 (D) [97.301e]
N1C11 (D) [97.301f]
N1D01 (A) [97.5d1]
N1D02 (D) [no ref]
N1D03 (C) [97.501e]
N1D04 (B) [97.21]

N1D05 (D) [97.27]
N1D06 (B) [97.19]
N1D07 (C) [no ref]
N1D08 (B) [no ref]
N1D09 (D) [no ref]
N1D10 (C) [97.23]
N1D11 (A) [97.19c]
N1E01 (A) [97.305/.307f9]
N1E02 (A) [97.305/307f9]
N1E03 (A) [97.305/307f9]
N1E04 (D) [97.305/307f9]
N1E05 (D) [97.305/307f9]
N1E06 (D) [97.305/307f9]
N1E07 (C) [97.305]
N1E08 (C)[97.305/307f10]
N1E09 (D) [97.305]
N1E10 (D) [97.305]
N1E11 (D)[97.305/.307f10]
N1E12 (C) [97.305]
N1E13 (B) [97.301e/.305]
N1E14 (B) [97.301e/.305]
N1F01 (D) [97.313a]
N1F02 (C) [97.313c1]
N1F03 (C) [97.313c1]
N1F04 (C) [97.313c1]
N1F05 (C) [97.313c2]
N1F06 (C) [97.313c2]
N1F07 (B) [97.313d]
N1F08 (A) [97.313e]
N1F09 (A) [97.313c]
N1F10 (C) [97.313d]
N1F11 (D) [97.313e]
N1G01 (D) [97.3a11]
N1G02 (C) [97.103a]
N1G03 (A) [97.103a]
N1G04 (D) [97.103a]
N1G05 (C) [97.103b]
N1G06 (B) [97.103]

N1G07 (A) [97.105b]
N1G08 (B) [97.105b]
N1G09 (C) [97.7]
N1G10 (A) [97.109b]
N1G11 (B) [97.109b]
N1H01 (D) [97.5a]
N1H02 (C) [97.111]
N1H03 (A) [97.113a]
N1H04 (A) [97.113a]
N1H05 (B) [97.113a]
N1H06 (C) [97.119a]
N1H07 (B) [97.119a]
N1H08 (A) [97.119a]
N1H09 (C) [97.119a]
N1H10 (B) [97.115c]
N1H11 (B) [97.119a]
N1I01 (A) [97.3a39]
N1I02 (D) [97.111a1]
N1I03 (C) [97.3a36]
N1I04 (B)
N1I05 (D) [97.113b]
N1I06 (A) [97.113c]
N1I07 (A) [97.113d]
N1I08 (C) [97.113d]
N1I09 (B) [97.3a42]
N1I10 (A) [97.115a2]
N1I11 (D) [97.115a2]
N1J01 (B) [97.3a21]
N1J02 (B) [97.3a21]
N1J03 (C) [97.101d]
N1J04 (A) [97.113d]
N1J05 (C) [97.113d]
N1J06 (C) [97.119a]
N1J07 (A) [97.119a]
N1J08 (D) [97.405a]
N1J09 (D) [97.119a]
N1J10 (C) [97.403]
N1J11 (B) [97.405a]

CHAPTER 2	N4A03 (A)	N5A07 (B)	N6A11 (C)	N8A11 (A)
N2A01 (A)	N4A04 (D)	N5A08 (B)	N6A12 (B)	**N8B01 (C)**
N2A02 (D)	N4A05 (C)	N5A09 (C)	**N6B01 (A)**	N8B02 (A)
N2A03 (C)	N4A06 (D)	N5A10 (C)	N6B02 (B)	N8B03 (C)
N2A04 (D)	N4A07 (B)	N5A11 (B)	N6B03 (A)	N8B04 (D)
N2A05 (B)	N4A08 (A)	**N5B01 (D)**	N6B04 (D)	N8B05 (D)
N2A06 (B)	N4A09 (C)	N5B02 (C)	N6B05 (A)	N8B06 (A)
N2A08 (D)	N4A10 (B)	N5B03 (B)	N6B06 (C)	N8B07 (B)
N2A09 (A)	N4A11 (C)	N5B04 (A)	N6B07 (D)	N8B08 (B)
N2A10 (A)	**N4B01 (B)**	N5B05 (A)	N6B08 (A)	N8B09 (B)
N2A11 (B)	N4B02 (A)	N5B06 (C)	N6B09 (B)	N8B10 (B)
N2A12 (B)	N4B03 (C)	N5B07 (C)	N6B10 (A)	N8B11 (D)
N2A13 (C)	N4B04 (A)	N5B08 (A)	N6B11 (C)	**CHAPTER 9**
N2A14 (D)	N4B05 (B)	N5B09 (B)	**CHAPTER 7**	**N9A01 (D)**
N2A15 (B)	N4B06 (D)	N5B10 (D)	**N7A01 (B)**	N9A02 (B)
N2A16 (D)	N4B07 (D)	N5B11 (D)	N7A02 (C)	N9A03 (A)
N2A17 (C)	N4B08 (D)	**N5C01 (A)**	N7A03 (D)	N9A04 (C)
N2A18 (C)	N4B09 (D)	N5C02 (C)	N7A04 (B)	N9A05 (D)
N2B01 (B)	N4B10 (A)	N5C03 (B)	N7A05 (D)	N9A06 (B)
N2B02 (B)	N4B11 (C)	N5C04 (A)	N7A06 (D)	N9A07 (C)
N2B03 (C)	**N4C01 (C)**	N5C05 (C)	N7A07 (A)	N9A08 (A)
N2B04 (D)	N4C02 (D)	N5C06 (C)	N7A08 (A)	N9A09 (B)
N2B05 (A)	N4C03 (A)	N5C07 (B)	N7A09 (B)	N9A10 (A)
N2B06 (B)	N4C04 (B)	N5C08 (C)	N7A10 (A)	N9A11 (B)
N2B07 (A)	N4C05 (C)	N5C09 (D)	N7A11 (B)	**N9B01 (B)**
N2B08 (B)	N4C06 (D)	N5C10 (B)	N7A12 (C)	N9B02 (C)
N2B09 (C)	N4C07 (A)	N5C11 (A)	N7A13 (C)	N9B03 (D)
N2B10 (A)	N4C08 (A)	**N5D01 (D)**	**N7B01 (B)**	N9B04 (A)
N2B11 (D)	N4C09 (B)	N5D02 (A)	N7B02 (C)	N9B05 (B)
N2B12 (A)	N4C10 (C)	N5D03 (B)	N7B03 (B)	N9B06 (B)
N2B13 (C)	N4C11 (A)	N5D04 (B)	N7B04 (C)	N9B07 (B)
N2B14 (D)	**N4D01 (C)**	N5D05 (C)	N7B05 (D)	N9B08 (C)
N2B15 (B)	N4D02 (B)	N5D06 (B)	N7B06 (A)	N9B09 (C)
CHAPTER 3	N4D03 (C)	N5D07 (C)	N7B07 (C)	N9B10 (A)
N3A01 (A)	N4D04 (D)	N5D08 (C)	N7B08 (A)	N9B11 (B)
N3A02 (C)	N4D05 (B)	N5D09 (A)	N7B09 (C)	**N9C01 (D)**
N3A03 (B)	N4D06 (B)	N5D10 (A)	N7B10 (D)	N9C02 (B)
N3A04 (C)	N4D07 (A)	N5D11 (B)	N7B11 (B)	N9C03 (B)
N3A05 (D)	N4D08 (A)	**CHAPTER 6**	**CHAPTER 8**	N9C04 (A)
N3A06 (B)	N4D09 (A)	**N6A01 (B)**	**N8A01 (B)**	N9C05 (B)
N3A07 (A)	N4D10 (C)	N6A02 (D)	N8A02 (A)	N9C06 (D)
N3A08 (C)	N4D11 (A)	N6A03 (A)	N8A03 (C)	N9C07 (A)
N3A09 (C)	**CHAPTER 4**	N6A04 (B)	N8A04 (A)	N9C08 (B)
N3A10 (A)	**N5A01 (B)**	N6A05 (B)	N8A05 (B)	N9C09 (C)
N3A11 (A)	N5A02 (C)	N6A06 (C)	N8A06 (D)	N9C10 (D)
N3A12 (C)	N5A03 (D)	N6A07 (A)	N8A07 (D)	N9C11 (A)
CHAPTER 4	N5A04 (B)	N6A08 (D)	N8A08 (C)	
N4A01 (B)	N5A05 (C)	N6A09 (A)	N8A09 (D)	
N4A02 (A)	N5A06 (C)	N6A10 (D)	N8A10 (D)	

Element 3A (Technician)

CHAPTER 1

T1A01 (D) [97.3a12]
T1A02 (B) [97.3a12]
T1A03 (A) [97.19a/b]
T1A04 (A) [97.19c]
T1A05 (C) [97.301/305e]
T1A06 (C) [97.301a]
T1A07 (B) [97.301a]
T1A08 (A) [97.301a]
T1A09 (B) [97.301a]
T1A10 (D) [97.301e]
T1A11 (C) [97.301e]
T1B01 (C) [97.3b6]
T1B02 (D) [97.3b6]
T1B03 (B) [97.203c]
T1B04 (C) [97.303]
T1B05 (D) [97.303]
T1B06 (C) [97.303a]
T1B07 (A) [97.305a]
T1B08 (B) [97.305c]
T1B09 (A) [97.305c]
T1B10 (D) [97.313b]
T1B11 (A) [97.209b2]
T1C01 (A) [97.119e1]
T1C02 (C) [97.307f3/4]
T1C03 (D) [97.307]
T1C04 (B) [97.307f4]
T1C05 (C) [97.307f5]
T1C06 (C) [97.307f4]
T1C07 (B) [97.307f5]
T1C08 (A) [97.307f5]
T1C09 (D) [97.307f6]
T1C10 (B) [97.307f6]
T1C11 (C) [97.307f6]
T1D01 (A) [97.3a9]
T1D02 (B) [97.119b1]
T1D03 (C) [97.119b2]
T1D04 (C) [97.119b2]
T1D05 (B) [97.203a]
T1D06 (A) [97.205c]
T1D07 (D) [97.205c]
T1D08 (A) [97.205c]
T1D09 (C) [97.215a]
T1D10 (D) [97.215a]
T1D11 (B) [97.215c]
T1E01 (A) [97.3a10]

T1E02 (B) [97.3a10]
T1E03 (D) [97.113b]
T1E04 (B) [97.113d]
T1E05 (D) [97.113d]
T1E06 (C) [97.113d]
T1E07 (C) [97.113e]
T1E08 (D) [97.115a2]
T1E09 (A) [97.115b1]
T1E10 (A) [97.401a]
T1E11 (C) [97.401c]

CHAPTER 2

T2A01 (B)
T2A03 (A)
T2A04 (D)
T2A05 (B)
T2A06 (B)
T2A07 (D)
T2A08 (B)
T2A09 (A)
T2A10 (C)
T2A11 (A)
T2A12 (A)
T2A13 (C)
T2A14 (D)
T2A15 (A)
T2A16 (A)
T2A17 (B)
T2A18 (C)
T2B01 (C)
T2B02 (A)
T2B03 (C)
T2B04 (D)
T2B05 (C)
T2B06 (A)
T2B07 (B)
T2B08 (B)
T2B09 (A)
T2B10 (C)
T2B11 (D)
T2C01 (A)
T2C02 (D)
T2C03 (A)
T2C04 (C)
T2C05 (A)
T2C06 (D)
T2C07 (B)

T2C08 (D)
T2C09 (B)
T2C10 (B)
T2C11 (C)
T2C12 (C)

CHAPTER 3

T3A01 (A)
T3A02 (D)
T3A03 (A)
T3A04 (C)
T3A05 (A)
T3A06 (B)
T3A07 (B)
T3A08 (A)
T3A09 (D)
T3A10 (B)
T3A11 (C)
T3B01 (D)
T3B02 (B)
T3B03 (A)
T3B04 (B)
T3B05 (D)
T3B06 (C)
T3B07 (A)
T3B08 (B)
T3B09 (A)
T3B10 (C)
T3B11 (A)
T3C01 (C)
T3C02 (C)
T3C03 (B)
T3C04 (C)
T3C05 (A)
T3C06 (D)
T3C07 (B)
T3C08 (D)
T3C09 (D)
T3C10 (A)
T3C11 (D)

CHAPTER 4

T4A01 (C)
T4A02 (D)
T4A03 (B)
T4A04 (D)
T4A05 (C)
T4A06 (D)

T4A07 (B)	T4D04 (B)	T5B10 (A)	T7A06 (B)	T9A05 (A)
T4A08 (A)	T4D05 (A)	T5B11 (A)	T7A07 (D)	T9A06 (D)
T4A09 (A)	T4D06 (A)	**CHAPTER 6**	T7A08 (D)	T9A07 (B)
T4A10 (A)	T4D07 (D)	**T6A01 (B)**	T7A09 (B)	T9A08 (A)
T4A11 (A)	T4D08 (A)	T6A02 (C)	T7A10 (D)	T9A09 (D)
T4A12 (C)	T4D09 (B)	T6A03 (B)	T7A11 (C)	T9A10 (D)
T4A13 (B)	T4D10 (A)	T6A04 (A)	**CHAPTER 8**	T9A11 (A)
T4A14 (C)	T4D11 (D)	T6A05 (B)	**T8A01 (B)**	**T9B01 (B)**
T4A15 (B)	T4D12 (B)	T6A06 (A)	T8A02 (C)	T9B02 (C)
T4B01 (B)	T4D13 (D)	T6A07 (C)	T8A03 (B)	T9B03 (C)
T4B02 (C)	T4D14 (D)	T6A08 (C)	T8A04 (B)	T9B04 (D)
T4B03 (A)	T4D15 (B)	T6A09 (B)	T8A05 (D)	T9B05 (D)
T4B04 (A)	T4D16 (C)	T6A10 (A)	T8A06 (D)	T9B06 (D)
T4B05 (D)	**CHAPTER 5**	T6A11 (D)	T8A07 (A)	T9B07 (A)
T4B06 (D)	**T5A01 (D)**	**T6B01 (D)**	T8A08 (A)	T9B08 (B)
T4B07 (A)	T5A02 (D)	T6B02 (C)	T8A09 (D)	T9B09 (C)
T4B08 (B)	T5A03 (C)	T6B03 (D)	T8A10 (C)	T9B10 (C)
T4B09 (A)	T5A04 (C)	T6B04 (A)	T8A11 (B)	T9B11 (A)
T4B10 (B)	T5A05 (D)	T6B05 (A)	**T8B01 (A)**	**T9C01 (B)**
T4B11 (C)	T5A06 (A)	T6B06 (B)	T8B02 (A)	T9C02 (A)
T4C01 (A)	T5A07 (B)	T6B07 (D)	T8B03 (A)	T9C03 (B)
T4C02 (A)	T5A08 (B)	T6B08 (D)	T8B04 (B)	T9C04 (A)
T4C03 (D)	T5A09 (A)	T6B09 (A)	T8B05 (C)	T9C05 (C)
T4C04 (B)	T5A10 (C)	T6B10 (C)	T8B06 (D)	T9C06 (B)
T4C05 (C)	T5A11 (A)	T6B11 (C)	T8B07 (C)	T9C07 (B)
T4C06 (C)	**T5B01 (D)**	T6B12 (B)	T8B08 (D)	T9C08 (D)
T4C07 (B)	T5B02 (C)	T6B13 (A)	T8B09 (C)	T9C09 (D)
T4C08 (D)	T5B03 (B)	T6B14 (B)	T8B10 (B)	T9C10 (C)
T4C09 (A)	T5B04 (C)	**CHAPTER 7**	T8B11 (C)	T9C11 (A)
T4C10 (A)	T5B05 (D)	**T7A01 (C)**	**CHAPTER 9**	
T4C11 (C)	T5B06 (D)	T7A02 (A)	**T9A01 (C)**	
T4D01 (D)	T5B07 (B)	T7A03 (A)	T9A02 (A)	
T4D02 (B)	T5B08 (D)	T7A04 (C)	T9A03 (C)	
T4D03 (C)	T5B09 (A)	T7A05 (D)	T9A04 (B)	

AVAILABLE FROM NARA

The Flight of OSCAR One

The first OSCAR satellite was little more than an orbiting shoe-box. But it carried aloft far more than just a keyer and transmitter—it also held the dreams of Amateurs everywhere for a new era in communications. Today we enjoy worldwide contacts via sophisticated OSCARs orbiting tens-of-thousands of kilometers above the earth. Relive the launch of OSCAR One from Vandenberg Air Force Base—hear the excitement of the dedicated hams who operated the OSCAR net and listen to its greeting message, HI, as it whirled around the globe in 1961. Your cost of this historic recording is only **$6.95 ($1.50 S&H)**. A true collector's item.

A **FREE** issue of *The Amateur Radio Communicator* will be sent to you when you order any product from NARA! Your magazine will be mailed at a later date.

Amateur Radio— King of Hobbies

A great publication to hand out at public events or whenever people ask "What is Amateur Radio and how do I get started?" It covers what ham radio is; who ham radio operators are; the various types of operations that ham radio operators engage in and tells the reader how to get a ham license. The publication also includes an extensive list of the Contact Volunteer Examiners, so anyone wanting a license can find someone in their local area to contact.

Attention Ham Dealers and Hobby Store Owners! This publication is a great way to attract people to your business and save valuable staff time by explaining what Amateur Radio is all about.

- 10 copies **$3.50 ($2.00 S&H)** #K800
- 20 copies **$7.00 (2.50 S&H)** #K801
- 50 copies **$17.50 ($3.00 S&H)** #K802

NEW!

Amateur Radio Mail Order Catalog And Resource Directory

This highly valuable reference directory contains over 1,500 entries, in 185 categories of Amateur radio resources! You'll find names, address' and phone numbers on everything from Alternative energy to Zener diodes. Including parts and equipment, kits and keyers, even personalized hats, mugs and license plates. There is even an extensive listing of radio clubs worldwide, international radio magazines, and over 100 free catalogs available.

If you're looking for that hard-to-find antenna or the perfect gift for that ham in your life, it's all right here at your fingertips in this 236-page Amateur radio resource catalog. An absolute must for every Amateur to own! **Amateur Radio Mail Order Catalog and Resource Directory is only $14.95 ($3.00 S&H) #B660**

Practice The Code With These Outstanding Code Tapes!

These tapes will help give you the practice you need to pass your code exams. Each set contains two cassette tapes.

- Novice/Technician Class 0 to 5wpm #T710.
- General Class 5 to 14wpm #T720
- Extra Class 12 to 24wpm #T730.

Order your set today for only **$11.95 ($2.00**

Order Today!

Order From NARA Toll Free

1-800-GOT-2-HAM (1-800-468-2426)

Index